Periodic GCSE Science revision from CGP!

There's a lot to learn for AQA's Grade 9-1 GCSE Combined Science exams...
sometimes it can be hard to get motivated for a big revision session.

That's why we've made this fantastic book — it's brimming with bite-sized tests
covering every topic from the Higher Level course. And since they only take
ten minutes each, they won't take over your life (unless you're really keen).

To round things off, all the answers are included at the back, along with a
chart to keep track of your marks. It's a brilliant revision companion!

CGP — still the best ☺

Our sole aim here at CGP is to produce the highest quality books
— carefully written, immaculately presented and
dangerously close to being funny.

Then we work our socks off to get them out to you
— at the cheapest possible prices.

Published by CGP

Editors:
Sarah Armstrong, Charlotte Burrows, Daniel Fielding, Emily Garrett, Sharon Keeley-Holden, Charles Kitts, Duncan Lindsay, Rachael Rogers, Ethan Starmer-Jones and Dawn Wright.

ISBN: 978 1 78294 847 6

With thanks to Susan Alexander, Mark Edwards, Emily Forsberg, Jamie Sinclair, Hayley Thompson and Sarah Williams for the proofreading.
With thanks to Emily Smith for the copyright research.

Clipart from Corel®
Printed by Elanders Ltd, Newcastle upon Tyne

Based on the classic CGP style created by Richard Parsons.

Contents

Biology Paper 1

Test 1: Cell Biology...2

Test 2: Organisation...4

Test 3: Organisation...6

Test 4: Infection and Response...........................8

Test 5: Infection and Response.........................10

Test 6: Bioenergetics..12

Test 7: Bioenergetics..14

Test 8: Biology 1 Mixed Topics.........................16

Test 9: Biology 1 Mixed Topics.........................18

Biology Paper 2

Test 10: Homeostasis and Response................20

Test 11: Homeostasis and Response................22

Test 12: Inheritance, Variation and Evolution....24

Test 13: Inheritance, Variation and Evolution....26

Test 14: Ecology...28

Test 15: Ecology...30

Test 16: Biology 2 Mixed Topics.......................32

Test 17: Biology 2 Mixed Topics.......................34

Chemistry Paper 1

Test 18: Atomic Structure and the Periodic Table......36

Test 19: Bonding, Structure and Properties.....38

Test 20: Bonding, Structure and Properties.....40

Test 21: Quantitative Chemistry........................42

Test 22: Chemical Changes...............................44

Test 23: Energy Changes...................................46

Test 24: Chemistry 1 Mixed Topics..................48

Test 25: Chemistry 1 Mixed Topics..................50

Chemistry Paper 2

Test 26: Rate and Extent of Chemical Change..........52

Test 27: Rate and Extent of Chemical Change.........54

Test 28: Organic Chemistry...............................56

Test 29: Chemical Analysis................................58

Test 30: Chemistry of the Atmosphere.............60

Test 31: Chemistry of the Atmosphere.............62

Test 32: Using Resources..................................64

Test 33: Chemistry 2 Mixed Topics..................66

Test 34: Chemistry 2 Mixed Topics..................68

Physics Paper 1

Test 35: Energy...70

Test 36: Energy...72

Test 37: Electricity..74

Test 38: Electricity..76

Test 39: Particle Model of Matter......................78

Test 40: Atomic Structure..................................80

Test 41: Physics 1 Mixed Topics.......................82

Test 42: Physics 1 Mixed Topics.......................84

Physics Paper 2

Test 43: Forces...86

Test 44: Forces...88

Test 45: Forces...90

Test 46: Waves...92

Test 47: Waves...94

Test 48: Magnetism and Electromagnetism.....96

Test 49: Physics 2 Mixed Topics.......................98

Test 50: Physics 2 Mixed Topics.....................100

Answers...102

Progress Chart..111

Biology Paper 1

Test 1: Cell Biology

There are **11 questions** in this test. Give yourself **10 minutes** to answer them all.

1. True or False? "All plant cells lose the ability to differentiate at an early stage."

    A True

    B False

    [1]

2. Which of these parts are not found in a bacterial cell?

    A Nucleus

    B Cell membrane

    C Cell wall

    [1]

3. Diffusion is where particles spread out from...

    A ... an area of lower concentration to an area of higher concentration.

    B ... an area of higher concentration to an area of lower concentration.

    [1]

4. When using a light microscope to view a slide, which lens should be selected to start with?

    A Lowest-powered objective lens

    B Highest-powered objective lens

    [1]

5. True or False? "In human body cells, chromosomes usually come in pairs."

    A True

    B False

    [1]

6. If the concentration of water inside a cell is lower than outside the cell, what will the net movement of water molecules be?

    A Into the cell

    B Out of the cell

    [1]

7. Which of these characteristics makes the alveoli efficient at gas exchange?

    A They have thick walls.

    B They have a large surface area.

    C They don't have a good blood supply.

    [1]

8. What happens inside a cell before mitosis takes place?

    A The number of subcellular structures it has increases.

    B One set of chromosomes is pulled to each end of the cell.

    C The cell membrane divides.

    [1]

9. Explain one way in which a nerve cell is adapted to carry out its specialised function.

....

....
[1]

10. What is a stem cell?

....

....

....
[2]

11. Complete this diagram of an animal cell.

Describe the roles of the following parts of a cell:

Mitochondria ....

....

Nucleus ....

....
[4]

15

Biology Paper 1: Cell Biology

4

Test 2: Organisation

There are **12 questions** in this test. Give yourself **10 minutes** to answer them all.

1. What is a tissue?

    A   A collection of different types of cell that work together.

    B   A collection of similar cells that work together.

    [1]

2. What colour is iodine solution in the presence of starch?

    A   Blue-black

    B   Browny-orange

    C   Brick-red

    [1]

3. Where is bile produced and stored?

    A   Bile is produced in the liver and stored in the gall bladder.

    B   Bile is produced in the gall bladder and stored in the stomach.

    C   Bile is produced in the stomach and stored in the pancreas.

    [1]

4. True or False? "People who have problems with their immune system have an increased chance of suffering from communicable diseases."

    A   True

    B   False

    [1]

5. Which type of tumour is cancerous?

    A   Benign

    B   Malignant

    [1]

6. Which of these is not a chamber of the heart?

    A   Left ventricle

    B   Right atrium

    C   Vena cava

    [1]

7. Which of these aren't features of arteries?

    A   Elastic fibres

    B   Thick walls

    C   Valves

    [1]

8. What's the function of palisade mesophyll tissue?

    A   It covers the surface of a plant.

    B   It's where photosynthesis happens.

    C   It carries substances around a plant.

    [1]

9. What is the role of protease enzymes?

....

....

[1]

10. Describe the function of phloem tissue.

....

....

[1]

11. Give two components of blood that are carried in the blood plasma.

1. ....

2. ....

[2]

12. Describe what happens to an enzyme if the temperature is too high.

....

....

....

....

[3]

15

Test 3: Organisation

There are **12 questions** in this test. Give yourself **10 minutes** to answer them all.

1. True or False? "Organ systems work together to form organs."

    A True

    B False

    [1]

2. What artificial device can be used to keep arteries open and blood flowing?

    A A ventilator

    B A valve

    C A stent

    [1]

3. When breathing in, which structure(s) does air enter first?

    A Alveoli

    B Trachea

    C Bronchi

    [1]

4. What is the function of white blood cells?

    A They deliver nutrients around the body.

    B They transport deoxygenated blood around the body.

    C They defend the body against microorganisms.

    [1]

5. Why is the shape of an enzyme important for its function?

    A So that it can squeeze through small gaps.

    B So that it can enter the cells of the body.

    C So that it fits the substance involved in the reaction it is catalysing.

    [1]

6. What is the name of the cells that control the opening and closing of stomata?

    A Palisade cells

    B Guard cells

    C Meristem cells

    [1]

7. True or False? "Blood flows to the organs through veins."

    A True

    B False

    [1]

8. Which of the following would you use to test for the presence of protein?

    A Biuret solution

    B Benedict's solution

    C Iodine solution

    [1]

9. Give one advantage of using an artificial heart rather than transplanting a natural one.

....

....

[1]

10. Give one risk factor that can increase a person's chance of developing liver disease.

....

[1]

11. Describe what a benign tumour is.

....

....

[1]

12. Explain how increasing air movement around a plant's leaves would affect the rate of transpiration.

....

....

....

....

[4]

15

Test 4: Infection and Response

There are **11 questions** in this test. Give yourself **10 minutes** to answer them all.

1. What is the first stage of testing a new medicinal drug?

   A   The drug is tested on human cells and tissues in the lab.

   B   The drug is tested on human volunteers in a clinical trial.

[1]

2. How does the stomach help to defend the body against pathogens?

   A   It secretes hydrochloric acid to kill pathogens.

   B   It contains hairs to trap pathogens.

   C   It secretes antibodies to kill pathogens.

[1]

3. What's a microorganism that causes disease called?

   A   An antibody

   B   An antitoxin

   C   A pathogen

[1]

4. Which type of pathogen causes rose black spot on leaves?

   A   A fungus

   B   A bacterium

   C   A virus

[1]

5. Which drug was developed by Alexander Fleming?

   A   Penicillin

   B   Digitalis

   C   Aspirin

[1]

6. Gonorrhoea is a disease caused by...

   A   ... protists.

   B   ... viruses.

   C   ... bacteria.

[1]

7. True or False? "Antibiotics can kill viruses."

   A   True

   B   False

[1]

8. Which type of drugs are used to control HIV?

   A   Antibiotics

   B   Antiretrovirals

   C   Painkillers

[1]

9. Explain why the tobacco mosaic virus (TMV) affects the growth of plants.

....

....

....

[2]

10. Explain how mosquito nets help to prevent the spread of malaria.

....

....

....

[2]

11. Explain how vaccination can protect against a disease.

....

....

....

....

[3]

15

Test 5: Infection and Response

There are **11 questions** in this test. Give yourself **10 minutes** to answer them all.

1. What is penicillin?

    A An antibiotic

    B An anti-viral drug

    C A painkiller

    [1]

2. True or False? "For a large outbreak of an infectious disease to be prevented, everyone must be vaccinated against it."

    A True

    B False

    [1]

3. Which disease in humans can be partly controlled by vaccinating poultry against the pathogen?

    A Salmonella food poisoning

    B Gonorrhoea

    C Measles

    [1]

4. Which of the following diseases is not spread by sexual contact?

    A HIV

    B Gonorrhoea

    C Measles

    [1]

5. What do white blood cells produce to help defend against pathogens?

    A Antigens

    B Antibiotics

    C Antibodies

    [1]

6. Which of the following diseases is caused by a protist?

    A Measles

    B Malaria

    C HIV

    [1]

7. Which of these statements about bacteria is false?

    A Bacteria damage cells by living and replicating inside them.

    B Some bacteria reproduce really quickly in the body.

    C Bacteria can produce toxins.

    [1]

8. True or False? "Preclinical trials help to find the optimum dose for a drug."

    A True

    B False

    [1]

9. How do viruses make you feel ill?

....

....

....

[2]

10. How does the nose help to defend the body against disease?

....

....

[2]

11. What is a double-blind trial and why is it used in clinical trials?

....

....

....

....

....

[3]

15

Test 6: Bioenergetics

There are **12 questions** in this test. Give yourself **10 minutes** to answer them all.

1. During exercise, which of the following happens?

   A   Just your breathing rate increases.

   B   Just your breath volume increases.

   C   Your breathing rate and your breath volume increases.

   [1]

2. Which of these is not a limiting factor of photosynthesis?

   A   Light

   B   Temperature

   C   Oxygen

   [1]

3. True or False? "Aerobic respiration occurs in plants and animals all the time."

   A   True

   B   False

   [1]

4. True or False? "The starch in plants that's created from glucose is insoluble."

   A   True

   B   False

   [1]

5. Which type of respiration transfers more energy?

   A   Aerobic respiration

   B   Anaerobic respiration

   [1]

6. Respiration is an...

   A   ... exothermic reaction.

   B   ... endothermic reaction.

   [1]

7. Aerobic respiration produces...

   A   ... glucose.

   B   ... carbon dioxide only.

   C   ... water and carbon dioxide.

   [1]

8. What would you expect to happen to the volume of oxygen produced by pondweed if light intensity increased, and it was the limiting factor?

   A   It would increase.

   B   It would stay the same.

   C   It would decrease.

   [1]

9. Why do muscles start respiring anaerobically during vigorous exercise?

....

....

[1]

10. Name the supporting material that plants make using glucose.

....

Which part of the cell is made using this material?

....

[2]

11. Complete the equation for photosynthesis.

....

.... + water $\longrightarrow$ .... + oxygen

[2]

12. Describe how the body gets rid of the lactic acid that builds up in the muscles.

....

....

....

[2]

15

Test 7: Bioenergetics

There are **12 questions** in this test. Give yourself **10 minutes** to answer them all.

1. True or False? "Anaerobic respiration requires oxygen."

   A True

   B False

   [1]

2. Alex walked to catch the bus, but Peter was late so had to run. Whose heart rate will be higher?

   A Alex

   B Peter

   [1]

3. Which of these things are not used by plants to make proteins?

   A Glucose

   B Nitrate ions

   C Lipids

   [1]

4. Other than oxygen, what does photosynthesis produce?

   A Carbon dioxide

   B Water

   C Glucose

   [1]

5. True or False? "As the level of carbon dioxide increases, the rate of photosynthesis will always increase."

   A True

   B False

   [1]

6. Which chemical symbol represents a product of aerobic respiration?

   A $C_6H_{12}O_6$

   B O_2

   C CO_2

   [1]

7. Which of the following is produced when yeast cells respire anaerobically?

   A Glucose

   B Ethanol

   C Lactic acid

   [1]

8. What is a single lipid molecule made up of?

   A One molecule of glycerol and three fatty acids.

   B One fatty acid and three molecules of glycerol.

   C Three molecules of glycerol and three fatty acids.

   [1]

9. What is meant by the term 'metabolism'?

    ....

    ....
    [1]

10. Explain what happens to the rate of photosynthesis if a plant is put in a dark place.

    ....

    ....

    ....
    [2]

11. Describe what is meant by muscle fatigue and state when it occurs.

    ....

    ....

    ....
    [2]

12. Give two uses of the energy produced by respiration.

    1. ....

    ....

    2. ....

    ....
    [2]

    15

Biology Paper 1: Bioenergetics

Test 8: Biology 1 Mixed Topics

There are **11 questions** in this test. Give yourself **10 minutes** to answer them all.

1. True or False? "Increasing the temperature always causes the rate of photosynthesis to increase."

   A True

   B False

   [1]

2. Which type of microscope has a higher magnification?

   A Electron microscope

   B Light microscope

   [1]

3. Stem cells from adult bone marrow can turn into...

   A ... any type of cell.

   B ... many types of cell.

   C ... blood cells only.

   [1]

4. Why is a new drug tested on live animals?

   A Because it's cheaper than testing on humans.

   B To test how well the drug works compared to a placebo.

   C To make sure it's safe before testing on humans.

   [1]

5. If you place a slice of potato in a solution that has a higher sugar concentration than the fluid inside the potato, the potato will...

   A ... release water and decrease in mass.

   B ... absorb water and increase in mass.

   [1]

6. True or False? "Severe physical illness can lead to the development of mental illness."

   A True

   B False

   [1]

7. What is the function of cellulose?

   A To strengthen the cell walls in plants

   B To make proteins

   C To help with respiration

   [1]

8. Chromosomes are...

   A ... a type of organelle where photosynthesis occurs.

   B ... really long molecules of DNA, which contain genes.

   C ... a type of cell involved in reproduction.

   [1]

---

9. Give two ways that an exchange surface in animals may be specialised for its function.

1. ....

2. ....

[2]

10. How do plants make proteins?

....

....

....

....

[2]

11. Malignant tumours are more dangerous than benign tumours.
    Explain why.

....

....

....

....

....

[3]

15

Test 9: Biology 1 Mixed Topics

There are **11 questions** in this test. Give yourself **10 minutes** to answer them all.

1. Which part of the blood is responsible for blood clotting?

   A Red blood cells

   B White blood cells

   C Platelets

   [1]

2. True or False? "Vaccinations involve injecting small amounts of dead or inactive pathogens into the body."

   A True

   B False

   [1]

3. True or False? "The DNA in plant cells is found within a nucleus."

   A True

   B False

   [1]

4. How are root cells specialised for absorbing water and nutrients?

   A They are round.

   B They have bacteria on their surface.

   C The cells are shaped like long hairs.

   [1]

5. True or False? "Some types of cancer can be triggered by a viral infection."

   A True

   B False

   [1]

6. What is a cell called when it has differentiated?

   A An unspecialised cell.

   B A specialised cell.

   C A stem cell.

   [1]

7. The leaf is an example of a plant...

   A ... tissue.

   B ... organ.

   C ... organ system.

   [1]

8. What happens to enzymes at high temperatures?

   A They divide, producing more enzymes.

   B They start to attack the cells in the body.

   C They denature.

   [1]

9. What is the function of xylem vessels?

....

Give one way in which they're adapted for this function.

....

....

[2]

10. A student investigates the effect of pH on the reaction rate of amylase on starch solution. Give one example of a variable that must be controlled in this investigation.

....

How could this variable be controlled?

....

[2]

11. Describe what happens in the heart of someone with coronary heart disease.

....

....

....

....

[3]

15

Test 10: Homeostasis and Response

There are **11 questions** in this test. Give yourself **10 minutes** to answer them all.

1. When a woman has a low level of FSH, her...

    A   ... uterus lining is not maintained.

    B   ... eggs do not mature.

    C   ... mature eggs are not stimulated
    to release.

    [1]

2. How many days does the menstrual cycle usually last for?

    A   52 days

    B   7 days

    C   28 days

    [1]

3. Reaction time is the time it takes for someone to...

    A   ... detect a stimulus.

    B   ... respond to a stimulus.

    C   ... remember something.

    [1]

4. Which of the following is an example of a coordination centre?

    A   The skin

    B   The pancreas

    C   A muscle

    [1]

5. Which of the following is a barrier method of contraception?

    A   Diaphragm

    B   Contraceptive patch

    C   Intrauterine device

    [1]

6. The gland which releases thyroxine is...

    A   ... the pituitary gland.

    B   ... the adrenal gland.

    C   ... the thyroid gland.

    [1]

7. What is the central nervous system made up of?

    A   The brain and receptors

    B   The brain and the spinal cord

    C   The spinal cord and receptors

    [1]

8. Which is the correct pathway for stimuli along a reflex arc?

    A   relay neurone → sensory neurone
    → motor neurone

    B   sensory neurone → motor neurone
    → relay neurone

    C   sensory neurone → relay neurone
    → motor neurone

    [1]

9. Give two roles that thyroxine has in the body.

    1. ....

    2. ....
    [2]

10. Explain what Type 1 diabetes is, and why it is dangerous.

    ....

    ....

    ....
    [2]

11. List three internal conditions that your body needs to keep constant to survive.

    1. ....

    2. ....

    3. ....
    [3]

15

Biology Paper 2: Homeostasis and Response

Test 11: Homeostasis and Response

There are **11 questions** in this test. Give yourself **10 minutes** to answer them all.

1. What is the hormone that controls the 'fight or flight' response?

   A   Thyroxine

   B   Adrenaline

   C   Glucagon

   [1]

2. True or False? "Caffeine can affect a person's reaction time."

   A   True

   B   False

   [1]

3. The contraceptive implant continuously releases progesterone, which...

   A   ... stimulates the production of FSH.

   B   ... stops the ovaries releasing eggs.

   C   ... acts as a spermicidal agent.

   [1]

4. In the menstrual cycle, what effect does the release of oestrogen have on LH and FSH?

   A   It stimulates the release of LH and FSH.

   B   It inhibits the release of LH and stimulates the release of FSH.

   C   It stimulates the release of LH and inhibits the release of FSH.

   [1]

5. Where in the body would you find the adrenal gland?

   A   In the neck

   B   In the brain

   C   Just above the kidneys

   [1]

6. True or False? "The blood sugar level of someone with Type 1 diabetes is always dangerously low."

   A   True

   B   False

   [1]

7. What is secreted by the pancreas when blood glucose levels fall?

   A   Glucose

   B   Insulin

   C   Glucagon

   [1]

8. True or False? "Hormones have longer-lasting effects than nervous impulses."

   A   True

   B   False

   [1]

9. What is the role of LH in the menstrual cycle?

....
[1]

10. What type of neurone transmits impulses to an effector in the nervous system?

....

Give an example of an effector, and describe how it responds to a stimulus.

....

....
[3]

11. What is meant by the term homeostasis?

....

....

....

....
[3]

15

Test 12: Inheritance, Variation and Evolution

There are **12 questions** in this test. Give yourself **10 minutes** to answer them all.

1. True or False? "Selective breeding can happen without human intervention."

   A True

   B False

   [1]

2. What effect do mutations have on variation?

   A They decrease it.

   B They increase it.

   C There is no effect.

   [1]

3. When an individual has one dominant and one recessive allele...

   A ... the recessive allele is expressed.

   B ... both alleles are expressed.

   C ... the dominant allele is expressed.

   [1]

4. True or False? "Fossils can be formed from an organism's footprints and burrows that have been preserved over time."

   A True

   B False

   [1]

5. How many chromosomes does a human gamete have?

   A 46

   B 12

   C 23

   [1]

6. What sex chromosomes does someone who is biologically male have?

   A XY

   B XXX

   C XX

   [1]

7. What is the main idea behind Darwin's theory of evolution by natural selection?

   A There is variation in a population. Those more suited to the environment will be more likely to survive and pass on their characteristics.

   B Individuals develop characteristics during their lifetimes, which make them more suited to their environment. They pass these onto their offspring.

   [1]

8. How are genes 'cut out' from chromosomes in genetic engineering?

   A Using enzymes

   B Using bacteria

   C Using a knife

   [1]

Biology Paper 2: Inheritance, Variation and Evolution

9. What is a fossil?

....

....

[1]

10. Give two pieces of evidence that support Darwin's theory of evolution.

1. ....

....

2. ....

....

[2]

11. Suggest two reasons why someone may be against embryonic screening.

1. ....

....

2. ....

....

[2]

12. Briefly describe the role of a vector in genetic engineering and give one example of a vector used.

....

....

....

[2]

15

Test 13: Inheritance, Variation and Evolution

There are **11 questions** in this test. Give yourself **10 minutes** to answer them all.

1. True or False? "The alleles for cystic fibrosis and polydactyly are both dominant."

   A True

   B False

[1]

2. If a farmer wants to increase the meat yield of his cows, he would breed together...

   A ... the biggest cows.

   B ... those that produced the most milk.

   C ... those with a gentle temperament.

[1]

3. What is an organism's genotype?

   A The characteristics that the organism has.

   B The alleles that the organism has.

[1]

4. How often do mutations result in a new phenotype?

   A Always

   B Often

   C Very rarely

[1]

5. What do evolutionary trees show?

   A Evolutionary relationships

   B Parental relationships

   C Genetic disorders

[1]

6. What is a problem that could result from patients not finishing a course of antibiotics?

   A Antibiotic resistance increases in bacteria.

   B Antibiotic resistance increases in viruses.

   C Immunity to disease increases in humans.

[1]

7. How many cell divisions occur during meiosis?

   A 1

   B 2

   C 4

[1]

8. What is the correct order of classification groups?

   A Kingdom → Genus → Class → Order → Family → Phylum → Species

   B Family → Phylum → Species → Order → Kingdom → Genus → Class

   C Kingdom → Phylum → Class → Order → Family → Genus → Species

[1]

---

9. A tall pea plant with two dominant 'T' alleles and a dwarf pea plant with two recessive
   't' alleles are crossed to produce a pea plant with the genotype Tt. What will the new
   plant's phenotype be? Explain your answer.

   ....

   ....

   ....

   ....

   [2]

10. The diagram shows a simple evolutionary tree.
    Use it to describe how the whale and shark are related,
    in terms of distant and recent ancestors.

    ....

    ....

    ....

    ....
    [2]

    Whale   Shark

11. Explain how sexual reproduction produces variation.

    ....

    ....

    ....

    ....

    ....

    [3]

    15

Biology Paper 2: Inheritance, Variation and Evolution

Test 14: Ecology

There are **12 questions** in this test. Give yourself **10 minutes** to answer them all.

1. What type of compost should people choose to avoid contributing to global warming?

    A   Peat-free compost

    B   Compost made using peat

    [1]

2. True or False? "In the water cycle, water falls from clouds in a process called evaporation."

    A   True

    B   False

    [1]

3. Which is the best definition of an extremophile?

    A   An organism that is able to live in only one type of environment.

    B   An organism that is adapted to living in very extreme conditions.

    C   An organism that is adapted to living in safe conditions.

    [1]

4. What does a change in the distribution of an animal mean?

    A   A change in its numbers.

    B   A change in where it lives.

    C   A change in the food it eats.

    [1]

5. Which of the following factors do plants compete for?

    A   Light, space, water and mates

    B   Water, mates, space and mineral ions

    C   Space, water, mineral ions and light

    [1]

6. True or False? "Global warming could reduce the Earth's biodiversity."

    A   True

    B   False

    [1]

7. Biodiversity is...

    A   ... all the organisms of one species living in a habitat.

    B   ... the interaction of a community of living organisms with the abiotic parts of their environment.

    C   ... the variety of different species on Earth.

    [1]

8. How do the population sizes of predators and prey change in a stable community?

    A   The size of the predator population continuously increases.

    B   The size of the prey population continuously decreases.

    C   The sizes of both populations rise and fall in cycles.

    [1]

9. What is meant by the term 'adaptation'?

....

....

[1]

10. Give two reasons why large-scale deforestation has occurred in tropical areas.

1. ....

2. ....

[2]

11. Give two ways that land can become polluted by humans.

1. ....

2. ....

[2]

12. Explain how draining peat bogs to produce compost contributes to global warming.

....

....

....

....

[2]

15

Biology Paper 2: Ecology

Test 15: Ecology

There are **12 questions** in this test. Give yourself **10 minutes** to answer them all.

1. How can you study the distribution of organisms in a way that will give reproducible results?

   A Always take the sample from the same place.

   B Use a small sample size.

   C Use a large sample size.

   [1]

2. What is global warming?

   A An increase in the level of oxygen within the Earth's atmosphere.

   B A decrease in the level of carbon dioxide within the Earth's atmosphere.

   C An increase in the average global temperature.

   [1]

3. True or False? "To study the effect of an abiotic factor on the distribution of an organism, you could use a transect."

   A True

   B False

   [1]

4. A species being outcompeted by another species is an example of...

   A ... a biotic factor.

   B ... an abiotic factor.

   [1]

5. Which of the following is an abiotic factor?

   A Temperature

   B New predators arriving

   C New pathogens arriving

   [1]

6. A producer...

   A ... is eaten by secondary consumers.

   B ... makes glucose from photosynthesis.

   C ... is also a primary consumer.

   [1]

7. True or False? "Sewage produced by humans can pollute lakes, rivers and oceans."

   A True

   B False

   [1]

8. If a new predator arrives in an area, will the size of the prey population increase or decrease?

   A Increase

   B Decrease

   [1]

9. What is interdependence?

....

....

[1]

10. How does respiration contribute to the carbon cycle?

....

[1]

11. Give two types of programme that people have set up to protect ecosystems and biodiversity.

1. ....

....

2. ....

....

[2]

12. Suggest three biotic factors that might cause a decrease in the population of a species.

1. ....

2. ....

3. ....

[3]

15

Test 16: Biology 2 Mixed Topics

There are **11 questions** in this test. Give yourself **10 minutes** to answer them all.

1. Which of these is a problem caused by the rapid rise in the world's population?

   A   Less carbon dioxide in the atmosphere

   B   More waste is being produced

   C   More diversity amongst people

   [1]

2. True or False? "Surgical sterilisation in males involves cutting the sperm duct and so is a permanent method of contraception."

   A   True

   B   False

   [1]

3. Deforestation is...

   A   ... growing crops in forests.

   B   ... renaming forests.

   C   ... cutting down trees.

   [1]

4. What combination of hormones can be given to a woman to improve her fertility?

   A   Oestrogen and progesterone

   B   FSH and LH

   C   Oestrogen and LH

   [1]

5. True or False? "The pituitary gland secretes hormones that act on other glands to trigger the release of other hormones."

   A   True

   B   False

   [1]

6. Which one of these things do animals not compete for in order to survive?

   A   Food

   B   Light

   C   Space

   [1]

7. The level of glucose in the blood is monitored by the...

   A   ... pancreas.

   B   ... thyroid gland.

   C   ... pituitary gland.

   [1]

8. What is the male gamete in plants called?

   A   Egg

   B   Stamen

   C   Pollen

   [1]

9. Give one use of genetically engineered bacteria in medicine.

   ....

   [1]

10. Explain why new, antibiotic-resistant strains of bacteria can quickly spread.

    ....

    ....

    ....

    [2]

11. Describe the process of *in vitro* fertilisation (IVF).

    ....

    ....

    ....

    ....

    ....

    [4]

15

Biology Paper 2: Mixed Topics

34

Test 17: Biology 2 Mixed Topics

There are **11 questions** in this test. Give yourself **10 minutes** to answer them all.

1. Which of the following may be used to control Type 2 diabetes?

   A Taking injections of glucagon.

   B Avoiding all forms of exercise.

   C Eating a carbohydrate-controlled diet.

   [1]

2. True or False? "An organism's characteristics can only be determined by the genes it has inherited."

   A True

   B False

   [1]

3. Which of the following is the main reproductive hormone in men?

   A Oestrogen

   B Progesterone

   C Testosterone

   [1]

4. What is a gene?

   A An amino acid

   B A protein

   C A small section of DNA

   [1]

5. Who developed the three-domain classification system?

   A Carl Linnaeus

   B Carl Woese

   C Charles Darwin

   [1]

6. True or False? "Some gametes are genetically identical to each other."

   A True

   B False

   [1]

7. What is meant when a reflex arc is described as 'automatic'?

   A It only involves the brain.

   B It only involves the conscious part of the brain.

   C It doesn't involve the conscious part of the brain.

   [1]

8. An ecosystem is the interaction...

   A ... between the individuals of a species that live in a habitat.

   B ... between the community of living organisms.

   C ... between the community of living organisms and the non-living parts of their environment.

   [1]

9. Why is it important for your body temperature to be maintained at a certain level?

....

....
[1]

10. Suggest two reasons why it is important to understand the human genome.

1. ....

....

2. ....

....
[2]

11. Rachael and Henry are about to have a child. Both of them carry the cystic fibrosis allele, but do not have the disease.
Complete the genetic diagram to show the possible genotypes of the child.

What is the chance that their child will have cystic fibrosis?
Explain your answer.

....

....

....
[4]

15

Biology Paper 2: Mixed Topics

⏱Test 18: Atomic Structure and the Periodic Table

There are **12 questions** in this test. Give yourself **10 minutes** to answer them all.

1. True or False? "The further down Group 7 you go, the more reactive the elements get."

   A True

   B False

   [1]

2. When using fractional distillation to separate a mixture of liquids in the lab, which liquid will be collected first?

   A The liquid with the lowest boiling point.

   B The liquid with the highest boiling point.

   C The most abundant liquid.

   [1]

3. What is a substance made of only one kind of atom called?

   A An element

   B A compound

   C A metal

   [1]

4. What is the name for the elements in Group 0 of the periodic table?

   A Alkali metals

   B Halogens

   C Noble gases

   [1]

5. Magnesium has 12 electrons. What will its electronic structure be?

   A 6, 6

   B 8, 4

   C 2, 8, 2

   [1]

6. True or False? "A group is a vertical column in the periodic table."

   A True

   B False

   [1]

7. Which of the following is a typical physical property of non-metals?

   A Good conductor of electricity

   B Malleable

   C Dull looking

   [1]

8. How did Niels Bohr suggest electrons were arranged in the atom?

   A Scattered within a ball of positive charge.

   B As a cloud surrounding the nucleus.

   C At fixed distances from the nucleus.

   [1]

9. In the modern periodic table, what do the electronic structures of elements in the same group have in common?

    ....
    [1]

10. Why do Group 1 elements become more reactive as you go down the group?

    ....

    ....

    ....
    [2]

11. Name the three different particles inside an atom and state the charge of each one.

    Particle: ....   Charge: ....

    Particle: ....   Charge: ....

    Particle: ....   Charge: ....
    [3]

12. Balance the following chemical equation:

    $$........Li + ...H_2O \rightarrow ....LiOH + ...H_2$$
    [1]

    15

Chemistry Paper 1: Atomic Structure and the Periodic Table

Test 19: Bonding, Structure and Properties

There are **12 questions** in this test. Give yourself **10 minutes** to answer them all.

1. What does a compound made up of a metal and a non-metal consist of?

A Atoms

B Molecules

C Ions

[1]

2. What type of structure does silicon dioxide have?

A Giant covalent

B Simple molecular

C Ionic lattice

[1]

3. True or False? "Pure metals are harder than alloys."

A True

B False

[1]

4. Giant covalent structures have...

A ... high melting points.

B ... low melting points.

[1]

5. What is a covalent bond?

A A pair of electrons shared between two atoms.

B A pair of electrons transferred from one atom to another.

C An attraction between two oppositely charged ions.

[1]

6. In substances containing small molecules...

A ... the intermolecular forces are much stronger than the covalent bonds within the molecules.

B ... the covalent bonds within the molecules are much stronger than the intermolecular forces.

C ... the covalent bonds within the molecules are the same strength as the intermolecular forces.

[1]

7. True or False? "Ionic compounds conduct electricity when dissolved in water but not when molten."

A True

B False

[1]

8. True or False? "Metals can conduct electricity because the ions in the metallic structure are free to move."

A True

B False

[1]

---

9. Describe the bonding in a Cl_2 molecule.

....

....

....
[2]

10. Describe the structure of sodium chloride.

....

....

....
[2]

11. Why are polymers usually solids at room temperature?

....

....
[1]

12. Explain, in terms of its structure, why graphite conducts electricity.

....

....

....
[2]

15

Test 20: Bonding, Structure and Properties

There are **12 questions** in this test. Give yourself **10 minutes** to answer them all.

1. Which of the following features is present in metallic bonding?

   A Delocalised electrons

   B A shared pair of electrons

   C Two oppositely charged ions

   [1]

2. Why do ionic compounds have high boiling points?

   A The bonds between the ions are weak.

   B It takes a lot of energy to break the bonds between the ions.

   [1]

3. In which state of matter are the particles closest together?

   A Gas

   B Liquid

   C Solid

   [1]

4. What is the overall charge on an ionic compound?

   A 0

   B −1

   C +1

   [1]

5. In the following example, what physical state is hydrochloric acid in?
   $$Mg_{(s)} + 2HCl_{(aq)} \rightarrow MgCl_{2(aq)} + H_{2(g)}$$

   A Solid

   B Gas

   C Aqueous

   [1]

6. Which term best describes the structure of diamond?

   A Sheets of carbon atoms arranged in hexagons

   B Giant covalent structure

   C Giant ionic lattice

   [1]

7. True or False? "Substances consisting of small molecules can conduct electricity."

   A True

   B False

   [1]

8. True or False? "The electronic structure of a chloride ion is 2, 8, 8."

   A True

   B False

   [1]

Chemistry Paper 1: Bonding, Structure and Properties

9. Describe how ions are formed when a metal reacts with a non-metal.

....

....

[1]

10. Describe the structure of fullerenes. Give one example of their use.

....

....

....

....

....

[3]

11. Explain the difference in hardness between pure metals and alloys.

....

....

[2]

12. Which of the substances in the table given below is a gas at 90 °C?

	Melting point (°C)	Boiling point (°C)
Ethanol	−114	78
Water	0	100
Iodine	114	184

....

[1]

15

Chemistry Paper 1: Bonding, Structure and Properties

Test 21: Quantitative Chemistry

There are **11 questions** in this test. Give yourself **10 minutes** to answer them all.

1. When a metal reacts completely to form a metal oxide, the mass of the metal oxide formed will be...

   A ... greater than the mass of the metal used.

   B ... less than the mass of the metal used.

   C ... the same as the mass of the metal used.

   [1]

2. True or False? "One mole of oxygen contains more molecules than one mole of hydrogen."

   A True

   B False

   [1]

3. What is the relative formula mass (M_r) of KOH?

   A 39

   B 28

   C 56

   [1]

4. True or False? "In a chemical reaction, the mass of the products is always less than the mass of the reactants."

   A True

   B False

   [1]

5. When taking repeat readings of an experiment, what does a large range of results suggest?

   A A small uncertainty in the results.

   B A large uncertainty in the results.

   C That the method used is accurate.

   [1]

6. True or False? "The more solute there is in a given volume the less concentrated the solution is."

   A True

   B False

   [1]

7. In the following reaction equation, what number should come before HCl to balance the equation?
   $Zn + HCl \rightarrow ZnCl_2 + H_2$

   A 1

   B 2

   C 3

   [1]

8. A reactant that is completely used up in a reaction is called the...

   A ... excess reactant.

   B ... limited reactant.

   C ... limiting reactant.

   [1]

9. Aluminium can be extracted from aluminium oxide via electrolysis.
Balance the equation for the reaction.

$$..... Al_2O_{3(l)} \rightarrow ..... Al_{(l)} + ... O_{2(g)}$$

[1]

10. Work out the mass of 2.5 mol of $Mg(OH)_2$.

Relative atomic masses (A_r): H = 1, O = 16, Mg = 24

....

....

....

.... g
[3]

11. Write a balanced symbol equation for the reaction when 140 g of iron reacts
with 80 g of oxygen gas to give iron oxide.

Relative atomic masses (A_r): O = 16, Fe = 56

....

....

....

....

Symbol equation:..
[3]

15

Test 22: Chemical Changes

There are **12 questions** in this test. Give yourself **10 minutes** to answer them all.

1. What does a pH of 7 indicate?

   A   An acidic solution

   B   An alkaline solution

   C   A neutral solution

   [1]

2. How can a solid salt be obtained from a salt solution?

   A   By adding an indicator.

   B   By adding a catalyst.

   C   By crystallisation of the salt solution.

   [1]

3. True or False? "Hydrochloric acid and magnesium react to produce magnesium chloride and hydrogen."

   A   True

   B   False

   [1]

4. In electrolysis, at the negative electrode, positively charged ions...

   A   ... lose electrons.

   B   ... gain electrons.

   C   ... dissolve.

   [1]

5. An alkaline solution of potassium hydroxide reacts with nitric acid to produce...

   A   ... carbon dioxide and water.

   B   ... a metal oxide and water.

   C   ... a salt and water.

   [1]

6. What can you say about the pH of a carbonic acid solution compared to that of a sulfuric acid solution with the same concentration?

   A   It's the same

   B   It's lower

   C   It's higher

   [1]

7. True or False? "Metals above carbon in the reactivity series can be extracted from their ore by reduction using carbon."

   A   True

   B   False

   [1]

8. Which reaction shows the oxidation of iron?

   A $Zn + FeSO_4 \rightarrow ZnSO_4 + Fe$

   B $Fe + CuSO_4 \rightarrow FeSO_4 + Cu$

   C $2Fe_2O_3 + 3C \rightarrow 4Fe + 3CO_2$

   [1]

9. Explain the difference between a strong acid and a weak acid in terms of ionisation.

....

....

[1]

10. Electrolysis can be used to extract aluminium from a molten mixture of aluminium oxide and cryolite. Describe the reactions that occur at the electrodes during this process.

Negative electrode: ....

....

Positive electrode: ....

....

[2]

11. Give the ionic equation for the reaction between hydrogen ions and hydroxide ions during a neutralisation reaction. Include state symbols in your answer.

....

[1]

12. Describe what you'd observe in the reactions of magnesium with dilute hydrochloric acid and iron with dilute hydrochloric acid. Give a reason for the difference between the two reactions.

....

....

....

....

....

[3]

15

Test 23: Energy Changes

There are **11 questions** in this test. Give yourself **10 minutes** to answer them all.

1. The reaction of citric acid and sodium hydrogencarbonate is...

   A   ... endothermic.

   B   ... exothermic.

   [1]

2. Which of these uses an endothermic reaction?

   A   Hand warmer

   B   Some sports injury packs

   C   Self heating drinks can

   [1]

3. True or False? "Energy is conserved in all chemical reactions."

   A   True

   B   False

   [1]

4. To break a chemical bond...

   A   ... energy must be supplied.

   B   ... energy must be released.

   [1]

5. In an endothermic reaction, the products are at...

   A   ... a lower energy than the reactants.

   B   ... a higher energy than the reactants.

   [1]

6. If the surroundings increase in temperature during a reaction...

   A   ... the reaction is endothermic.

   B   ... the reaction is exothermic.

   C   ... no new chemical bonds have formed.

   [1]

7. What is the activation energy of a reaction?

   A   The total energy of the reactants.

   B   The minimum amount of energy needed by the particles to react.

   C   The maximum amount of energy needed by the particles to react.

   [1]

8. Which of the following can be used to measure the energy change when a chemical reaction takes place?

   A   Change in colour

   B   Change in mass

   C   Change in temperature

   [1]

9. The equation below shows the combustion of methane.

$$CH_4 + 2O_2 \rightarrow CO_2 + 2H_2O$$

Here are the structures of methane, oxygen, carbon dioxide and water.

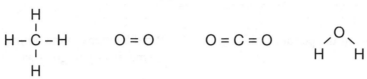

Using the bond energies below, work out the overall energy change
for the combustion of methane:

C – H: 413 kJ/mol,   O = O: 496 kJ/mol,   C = O: 803 kJ/mol,   O – H: 464 kJ/mol

....

....

....

....

.... kJ/mol
[3]

10. Give an example of a type of reaction that is exothermic.

....
[1]

11. The equation for the formation of hydrogen chloride is: $H_2 + Cl_2 \rightarrow 2HCl$
The overall energy change of this reaction is –184 kJ/mol.
Sketch a reaction profile for this reaction and label the overall energy change.

[3]   **15**

Test 24: Chemistry 1 Mixed Topics

There are **11 questions** in this test. Give yourself **10 minutes** to answer them all.

1. Why were early versions of the periodic table incomplete?

   A The First World War broke out before they could be finished.

   B The Church forbade their completion.

   C Some elements had not been discovered yet.

   [1]

2. What happens to the boiling points of the elements as you go down Group 0?

   A They decrease

   B They increase

   C They remain constant

   [1]

3. What is the mass of one mole of carbon?

   A 16 g

   B 6 g

   C 12 g

   [1]

4. Oxidation is...

   A ... gain of electrons.

   B ... loss of electrons.

   [1]

5. What is an exothermic reaction?

   A A reaction which transfers energy to the surroundings.

   B A reaction which takes in energy from the surroundings.

   [1]

6. True or False? "When forming an ionic bond, metal atoms lose electrons to form positive ions."

   A True

   B False

   [1]

7. Metal oxides are...

   A ... acids.

   B ... bases.

   [1]

8. Halogen X will displace halogen Y from an aqueous solution of its salt if halogen X is...

   A ... more reactive than halogen Y.

   B ... less reactive than halogen Y.

   [1]

9. State the two products formed in a reaction between a metal and an acid.

1. ....

2. ....

[2]

10. An element has the electronic structure 2, 8, 4.

Which group of the periodic table must it be in? Explain your answer.

....

....

[2]

11. 66 g of carbon are burnt completely in oxygen to produce CO_2.

The equation for the reaction is: $C + O_2 \rightarrow CO_2$.

Calculate the mass of CO_2 produced.

Relative atomic masses (A_r): C = 12, O = 16

....

....

....

....

.... g

[3]

15

Test 25: Chemistry 1 Mixed Topics

There are **12 questions** in this test. Give yourself **10 minutes** to answer them all.

1. An atom has a mass number of 23 and an atomic number of 11. How many neutrons does it have?

    A 11

    B 12

    C 23

    [1]

2. An ionic compound is made up of Na^+ ions and Br^- ions. What is its formula?

    A NaBr

    B Na_2Br

    C $NaBr_2$

    [1]

3. What is the pH scale used to measure?

    A The mass of a solution.

    B The temperature of a solution.

    C How acidic or alkaline a solution is.

    [1]

4. When a chemical bond forms...

    A ... energy must be supplied.

    B ... energy is released.

    [1]

5. Which of the following is an electrolyte?

    A A molten or dissolved ionic compound.

    B An electric current running through a solution.

    C A positively charged electrode.

    [1]

6. Which of these describes a metallic structure?

    A A giant structure of metal atoms held together by ionic bonds.

    B A giant structure of metal atoms arranged in an irregular pattern.

    C A giant structure of metal ions arranged in a regular pattern.

    [1]

7. True or False? "Soluble salts can be made by reacting an acid with a carbonate."

    A True

    B False

    [1]

8. The discovery of the electron led to the...

    A ... plum pudding atomic model.

    B ... Bohr atomic model.

    C ... modern nuclear atomic model.

    [1]

9. Does this energy level diagram show an exothermic or an endothermic reaction? Explain your answer.

Energy

Progress of Reaction

....

....
[2]

10. What is the concentration of the solution, in g/dm^3, if 0.25 g of NaOH are dissolved in 0.5 dm^3 of water?

....

....

....

.... g/dm^3
[2]

11. When would a metal displace another metal from an aqueous solution of its salt?

....
[1]

12. 1.84 g of ethanol (C_2H_5OH) is burnt completely in oxygen. Find the number of moles of carbon dioxide gas produced.

$$C_2H_5OH + 3O_2 \rightarrow 2CO_2 + 3H_2O$$

Relative formula mass (M_r) of C_2H_5OH = 46.

....

....

.... mol
[2]

15

Chemistry Paper 1: Mixed Topics

Test 26: Rate and Extent of Chemical Change

There are **11 questions** in this test. Give yourself **10 minutes** to answer them all.

1. What is a reversible reaction?

    A A reaction where the products of the
        reaction can react to produce further
        products.

    B A reaction where the products of the
        reaction can react to produce the original
        reactants.
                                              [1]

2. When a reversible reaction occurs in a sealed
    reaction vessel, when is equilibrium reached?

    A When all the reactants are used up.

    B When the amounts of products and
        reactants are equal.

    C When the rates of the forward and reverse
        reactions are equal.
                                              [1]

3. How does a catalyst increase a reaction's rate?

    A It shifts the position of equilibrium.

    B It increases the energy of the reactants.

    C It provides a different reaction pathway that
        has a lower activation energy.
                                              [1]

4. Which of these reactions would be faster?

    A Magnesium with concentrated
        hydrochloric acid

    B Magnesium with dilute hydrochloric acid
                                              [1]

5. The rate of a reaction doesn't depend on the...

    A ... frequency of collisions.

    B ... volume of solution.

    C ... temperature of the reactants.
                                              [1]

6. True or False? "A reversible reaction always
    takes in more energy in one direction than it
    gives out in the opposite direction."

    A True

    B False
                                              [1]

7. True or False? "Increasing the temperature of
    a reversible reaction will increase the yield of
    the exothermic reaction."

    A True

    B False
                                              [1]

8. Which of the following is not a unit of reaction
    rate?

    A g/s

    B cm^3/s

    C g/dm^3
                                              [1]

9. The diagram shows the results of the same
    reaction carried out in two different experiments.

    Suggest one way in which the conditions might
    have been different in experiment 2.
    Explain your answer.

    ....

    ....

    ....

    [2]

10. Magnesium reacts with hydrochloric acid to form magnesium chloride and hydrogen gas.
    Describe how you could determine the mean rate of this reaction.

    ....

    ....

    ....

    ....

    [3]

11. The equation below shows a reversible reaction, where A-D are different gases.

    $$2A + B \rightleftharpoons C + D$$

    Would the forwards or backwards reaction be favoured if the pressure were increased?
    Explain your answer.

    ....

    ....

    ....

    [2]

    15

Chemistry Paper 2: Rate and Extent of Chemical Change

Test 27: Rate and Extent of Chemical Change

There are **12 questions** in this test. Give yourself **10 minutes** to answer them all.

1. True or False? "The mean rate of reaction can be found by measuring the amount of reactant used over a period of time."

   A True

   B False

   [1]

2. Which of the following is a reason why increasing the temperature increases the rate of a reaction?

   A The reactant particles evaporate to form a gas.

   B The reactant particles move faster so they collide more frequently.

   C The reactant particles stick together more.

   [1]

3. What effect does adding a catalyst have on the overall energy change of a reaction?

   A It increases it.

   B It decreases it.

   C It has no effect.

   [1]

4. In a reaction between marble and hydrochloric acid, using small marble chips instead of a large piece of marble will produce...

   A ... no difference in the rate of reaction.

   B ... a faster rate of reaction.

   C ... a slower rate of reaction.

   [1]

5. In a reversible reaction, increasing the concentration of reactants will favour the reaction that forms...

   A ... more product until equilibrium is reached again.

   B ... less product until equilibrium is reached again.

   [1]

6. What effect will decreasing the temperature have on the yield of the exothermic reaction in a reversible reaction?

   A Increase it

   B Decrease it

   C Have no effect

   [1]

7. Which of the following affects the proportion of collisions that have enough energy for particles to react?

   A Gas pressure

   B Temperature

   C Concentration

   [1]

8. Halving the frequency of collisions in a reaction mixture...

   A ... halves the reaction rate.

   B ... decreases reaction rate by a factor of 4.

   C ... doubles the reaction rate.

   [1]

9. A reversible reaction is often said to be at equilibrium. What is meant by this?

....

....
[1]

10. The equation for the decomposition of hydrogen peroxide is shown below:

$$2H_2O_{2(aq)} \rightarrow 2H_2O_{(l)} + O_{2(g)}$$

How would you expect the total volume of O_2 produced to be affected by the presence of a catalyst? Explain your answer.

....

....

....
[2]

11. Explain, using collision theory, why increasing the concentration of a solution increases the rate of a reaction.

....

....

....
[2]

12. In a reaction between calcium and water, 10.2 cm³ of hydrogen gas is collected over the first 20 seconds. Calculate the mean rate of reaction during this time.

....

....

....
[2]

$$\boxed{\dfrac{}{15}}$$

Test 28: Organic Chemistry

There are **11 questions** in this test. Give yourself **10 minutes** to answer them all.

1. Crude oil is a...

   A ... renewable resource.

   B ... finite resource.

   C ... infinite resource.

   [1]

2. What is the general formula of an alkane?

   A C_nH_{2n}

   B C_nH_{2n+2}

   C C_2H_6

   [1]

3. What happens to bromine water when an alkene is added to it?

   A It turns cloudy.

   B It turns from colourless to orange.

   C It turns from orange to colourless.

   [1]

4. Which of the methods below could be used to crack a long-chain hydrocarbon?

   A Mix the hydrocarbon with water and add a cold platinum catalyst.

   B Mix the hydrocarbon vapour with steam and heat to a very high temperature.

   [1]

5. Which technique is used to separate the components of crude oil?

   A Cracking

   B Filtration

   C Fractional distillation

   [1]

6. What happens to the carbon and hydrogen in a fuel when it's burned?

   A They are oxidised.

   B They evaporate.

   C They react to form CH_4.

   [1]

7. True or False? "Cracking is used to turn long-chain hydrocarbons into short-chain hydrocarbons."

   A True

   B False

   [1]

8. Which alkane has the formula C_4H_{10}?

   A Methane

   B Ethane

   C Butane

   [1]

9. Write a balanced symbol equation for the complete combustion of propane, C_3H_8.

....

[2]

10. The formulas of two alkanes, decane and pentane, are shown below:

Decane: $C_{10}H_{22}$

Pentane: C_5H_{12}

Which of these alkanes will have the higher boiling point?
Explain your answer.

....

....

[2]

11. Vaporised crude oil is piped into the bottom of a fractionating column.
Explain how it is then separated into different fractions.

....

....

....

....

....

[3]

15

Chemistry Paper 2: Organic Chemistry

58

Test 29: Chemical Analysis

There are **12 questions** in this test. Give yourself **10 minutes** to answer them all.

1. What is the test for hydrogen?

    A It burns with a green flame.

    B It turns damp litmus paper white.

    C It burns with a pop.

    [1]

2. When carbon dioxide is bubbled through limewater, the limewater turns...

    A ... cloudy.

    B ... green.

    C ... yellow.

    [1]

3. True or False? "During paper chromatography, the paper must remain fully submerged in solvent."

    A True

    B False

    [1]

4. True or False? "Formulations are made for a specific purpose by mixing together exact amounts of different components."

    A True

    B False

    [1]

5. You can check if a substance is pure by...

    A ... testing its melting point.

    B ... using universal indicator solution.

    C ... shaking it with limewater.

    [1]

6. In chemistry, what is a pure substance?

    A A substance in its natural state.

    B A substance that only contains one compound or element.

    [1]

7. True or False? "Oxygen will relight a glowing splint."

    A True

    B False

    [1]

8. How many different phases are used in chromatography?

    A 1

    B 2

    C 3

    [1]

9. The melting point of a sample of water is –2 °C. Suggest why this is.

....
[1]

10. Describe the chemical test for chlorine.

....

....
[1]

11. A student carries out paper chromatography on a substance.
The solvent travelled 5.0 cm up the chromatography paper.
The substance left a spot 3.2 cm up the chromatography paper.
What is the R_f value of the substance?

....

....

....
[2]

12. Name the phases involved in chromatography.

....

Explain how the pattern of spots produced in a chromatography experiment
can be used to distinguish a pure substance from an impure substance.

....

....
[3]

$\dfrac{}{15}$

Test 30: Chemistry of the Atmosphere

There are **11 questions** in this test. Give yourself **10 minutes** to answer them all.

1. Why is sulfur often removed from fuels before they are burnt?

   A So the fuel produces less soot when it burns.

   B To reduce the cost of the fuel.

   C To reduce acid rain.

   [1]

2. Which of these is not produced when a fuel undergoes complete combustion?

   A Carbon monoxide

   B Carbon dioxide

   C Water

   [1]

3. Which of these is causing the average global temperature to rise?

   A An increasing amount of greenhouse gases in the atmosphere.

   B An increased amount of particulates in the atmosphere from car exhausts.

   C Large amounts of sulfur dioxide gas being released from burning fuels.

   [1]

4. It is difficult for scientists to be certain what the implications of global climate change will be because...

   A ... the evidence has not been peer-reviewed.

   B ... the Earth's climate is very complicated so is hard to model.

   C ... media reports are biased.

   [1]

5. True or False? "Nitrogen oxides form when fuels burn slowly at low temperatures."

   A True

   B False

   [1]

6. Which of the following is formed mainly from shells and skeletons of marine organisms?

   A Limestone

   B Coal

   C Crude oil

   [1]

7. Which of these gases is not a greenhouse gas?

   A Water vapour

   B Methane

   C Oxygen

   [1]

8. What percentage of the Earth's atmosphere is made up of oxygen?

   A About 80%

   B About 20%

   C Less than 1%

   [1]

9. Describe one way that governments can reduce carbon dioxide emissions.
    Give one reason why their actions are limited.

    ....

    ....

    ....

    ....
    [2]

10. Explain how the evolution of algae and green plants affected the composition of Earth's
    atmosphere.

    ....

    ....

    ....
    [2]

11. Which gas made up most of the Earth's early atmosphere?

    ....

    Name one other gas present in the Earth's early atmosphere.

    ....

    Where did these gases come from?

    ....
    [3]

    $$\boxed{\begin{array}{c} \\ \overline{15} \end{array}}$$

Chemistry Paper 2: Chemistry of the Atmosphere

Test 31: Chemistry of the Atmosphere

There are **10 questions** in this test. Give yourself **10 minutes** to answer them all.

1. True or False? "Greenhouse gases in the atmosphere help to keep temperatures on Earth high enough to support life."

   A True

   B False

   [1]

2. Which of these gases makes up the smallest proportion of our atmosphere?

   A Oxygen

   B Nitrogen

   C Carbon dioxide

   [1]

3. True or False? "We can reduce the carbon footprint of the power we use by using nuclear energy instead of fossil fuels."

   A True

   B False

   [1]

4. Solid particles in the atmosphere block some sunlight from reaching the Earth's surface. What is this effect called?

   A Global warming

   B Global dimming

   C Shadowing

   [1]

5. Carbon monoxide is...

   A ... a toxic gas.

   B ... a greenhouse gas.

   C ... a cause of acid rain.

   [1]

6. Which of these gases can cause respiratory problems?

   A Sulfur dioxide

   B Nitrogen

   C Carbon dioxide

   [1]

7. Which of the following is not a reason carbon dioxide levels decreased in the Earth's early atmosphere?

   A The formation of sedimentary rocks and fossil fuels that contain carbon.

   B The carbon dioxide reacted with oxygen in the atmosphere.

   C Algae and plants began to photosynthesise.

   [1]

8. Greenhouse gases...

   A ... absorb all wavelengths of radiation.

   B ... absorb short wavelength radiation from the Sun.

   C ... absorb long wavelength radiation from the Earth.

   [1]

9. How may rising global temperatures affect the polar ice caps?
Describe the consequences that this may have.

....

....

....

....

[3]

10. Give two human activities that increase the amount of methane in the atmosphere.
For each, explain why it causes an increase.

1. ....

....

2. ....

....

[4]

15

Test 32: Using Resources

There are **11 questions** in this test. Give yourself **10 minutes** to answer them all.

1. The main goal of a life cycle assessment is to assess...

   A ... the total environmental cost of a product.

   B ... the economic impact of a product.

   C ... how long a product will be in use.

   [1]

2. Why is bioleaching used to extract copper from its ore?

   A It's quicker than electrolysis.

   B It produces copper with fewer impurities than the copper produced by electrolysis.

   C It can be used on low-grade ores.

   [1]

3. What is phytomining?

   A A process that uses displacement reactions to extract copper.

   B A process that uses bacteria to separate metals from low-grade ores.

   C A process that uses plants to separate metals from low-grade ores.

   [1]

4. What is the first stage in making fresh water safe to drink?

   A Filtration

   B Distillation

   C Sterilisation

   [1]

5. True or False? "A life cycle assessment is an objective way to assess the environmental impact of a product and remove bias."

   A True

   B False

   [1]

6. Which of the following is an example of a renewable resource?

   A Copper

   B Wool

   C Nuclear fuel such as uranium

   [1]

7. True or False? "Potable water must contain no dissolved salts."

   A True

   B False

   [1]

8. Which process produces sewage sludge and effluent during sewage treatment?

   A Screening

   B Aerobic biological treatment

   C Sedimentation

   [1]

9. Describe two environmental impacts of extracting a metal from its ore.

1. ....

....

2. ....

....

[2]

10. Potable water can be produced from fresh water. This process involves sterilising the water to kill any harmful bacteria or microbes.
Give one way in which water can be sterilised.

....

[1]

11. What are the four stages of a product's life that are examined during a life cycle assessment?

1. ....

2. ....

3. ....

4. ....

[4]

15

Test 33: Chemistry 2 Mixed Topics

There are **11 questions** in this test. Give yourself **10 minutes** to answer them all.

1. True or False? "Increasing the pressure of the reaction $N_{2(g)} + 3H_{2(g)} \rightleftharpoons 2NH_{3(g)}$ favours the forward reaction."

    A True

    B False

    [1]

2. How many hydrogen atoms does ethane contain?

    A 2

    B 6

    C 8

    [1]

3. True or False? "Oxygen is the most abundant gas in the atmosphere."

    A True

    B False

    [1]

4. Which of these processes can be used to desalinate sea water?

    A Sterilisation

    B Reverse osmosis

    C Sedimentation

    [1]

5. Which of these effects on the planet is not associated with burning fossil fuels?

    A An increase in the average global temperature.

    B An increase in the amount of oxygen in the oceans.

    C An increase in the amount of carbon dioxide in the atmosphere.

    [1]

6. Which of these is used to test for the presence of an alkene?

    A Limewater

    B Bromine water

    C Sodium hydroxide solution

    [1]

7. Which of the following increases the rate of reaction?

    A Diluting the solution in which the reaction is happening.

    B Measuring the amount of gas evolved each second.

    C Increasing the average energy of the collisions.

    [1]

8. True or False? "Catalysts are used up during a reaction."

    A True

    B False

    [1]

9. Sedimentation is one of the processes used in sewage treatment.
During sedimentation, the sewage separates into two parts.
Name each part and state the process used to treated it.

Part 1: ....

Process used to treat it: ....

Part 2: ....

Process used to treat it: ....

[4]

10. Give two reasons why the levels of carbon dioxide in the early atmosphere of Earth
began to decrease.

1. ....

....

2. ....

....

[2]

11. Many fertilisers can be described as formulations. What does this mean?

....

....

[1]

15

Test 34: Chemistry 2 Mixed Topics

There are **11 questions** in this test. Give yourself **10 minutes** to answer them all.

1. True or False? "In chromatography, the R_f value for a substance will be the same no matter what solvent is used."

   A True

   B False

   [1]

2. True or False? "Taxing companies based on the amount of greenhouse gases they produce aims to increase the country's carbon footprint."

   A True

   B False

   [1]

3. Why can the hydrocarbons in crude oil be separated by fractional distillation?

   A They have different boiling points.

   B They have different melting points.

   C They have different viscosities.

   [1]

4. Which of the following cannot be used in showing that a sample of a substance is impure?

   A Melting or boiling point data

   B Chromatography

   C Crystallisation

   [1]

5. If a reversible reaction is endothermic in one direction, what will it be in the other direction?

   A Endothermic

   B Could be exothermic or endothermic

   C Exothermic

   [1]

6. Which of the following are produced by cracking?

   A Alkanes and water vapour

   B Alkanes and alkenes

   C Only alkanes

   [1]

7. After bioleaching, further processing is required to obtain copper metal. Which of these processes is not used for this?

   A Electrolysis

   B Phytomining

   C Displacement by iron

   [1]

8. True or False? "Increasing the pressure of any reaction mixture will increase the reaction rate."

   A True

   B False

   [1]

9. A certain reaction is carried out with and without a catalyst. Which line on the reaction profile shows the reaction with a catalyst? Explain your answer.

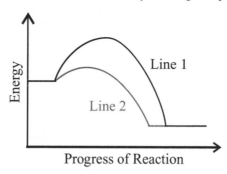

....

....
[2]

10. What is a selective life cycle assessment and how might it be misused by a company?

....

....

....
[2]

11. Using collision theory, explain how breaking a solid reactant up into smaller pieces will affect the rate of a reaction.

....

....

....

....
[3]

15

Test 35: Energy

There are **11 questions** in this test. Give yourself **10 minutes** to answer them all.

1. What happens to the amount of energy in a car's kinetic energy store when the car slows down?

   A It remains the same.

   B It decreases as some energy is transferred away to different energy stores.

   C It decreases as some energy is destroyed.

   [1]

2. Pick a suitable option that can be used to improve the efficiency of a battery-powered toy car.

   A Insulate the car.

   B Increase the input energy to the car.

   C Lubricate any moving parts in the car.

   [1]

3. When an object falls from a height, the maximum energy transferred to its kinetic energy store is equal to...

   A ... the energy transferred away from its gravitational potential energy store.

   B ... the energy transferred to its gravitational potential energy store.

   [1]

4. Which of these is a disadvantage of using wind turbines to generate electricity?

   A They can be noisy.

   B They release atmospheric pollution (CO_2) when running.

   C They produce dangerous waste that is difficult to dispose of.

   [1]

5. The amount of energy transferred by an appliance depends on...

   A ... its power and size.

   B ... its power and mass.

   C ... its power and the time it is on for.

   [1]

6. 800 J of energy is supplied to a toaster with an efficiency of 25%. What is the useful output of the toaster?

   A 200 J

   B 775 J

   C 1000 J

   [1]

7. When a racket hits a ball, energy is transferred from the racket's kinetic energy store to the ball's kinetic energy store. This energy is transferred...

   A ... by heating.

   B ... electrically.

   C ... mechanically.

   [1]

8. Two garages of equal size and shape have walls made of the same material. One garage has thicker walls than the other. They are heated to the same temperature then left to cool. Which garage would cool the fastest?

   A The one with thick walls.

   B The one with thin walls.

   [1]

9. A go-kart travels along a straight length of track at 8.5 m/s.
    The go-kart and its driver have a combined mass of 160 kg.
    Calculate the total energy in the kinetic energy stores of the go-kart and driver.

    ....

    ....

    Energy = ... J

    [2]

10. Describe two problems with generating electricity using nuclear power.

    1. ....

    ....

    2. ....

    ....

    [2]

11. 2925 J of energy is needed to increase the temperature of 500 g of copper by 15 °C.

    Calculate the specific heat capacity of copper.

    change in thermal energy = mass × specific heat capacity × temperature change

    ....

    ....

    ....

    ....

    Specific heat capacity = ... J/kg°C

    [3]

15

Physics Paper 1: Energy

Test 36: Energy

There are **11 questions** in this test. Give yourself **10 minutes** to answer them all.

1. Power is the...

   A   ... conservation of momentum.

   B   ... energy of a moving object.

   C   ... rate of doing work.

   [1]

2. When a spring is compressed, which of these energy stores is energy transferred to?

   A   The spring's elastic potential energy store

   B   The spring's nuclear energy store

   C   The spring's magnetic energy store

   [1]

3. What is the name of a system in which there is no net change in the total energy?

   A   A closed system

   B   An open system

   C   A mechanical system

   [1]

4. Two materials with the same mass and different specific heat capacities are cooled by 10° C. Which material emits more energy?

   A   The material with the lower specific heat capacity

   B   The material with the higher specific heat capacity

   [1]

5. The rate of energy transfer from a house can be reduced by...

   A   ... having walls with a low thermal conductivity.

   B   ... having walls with a high thermal conductivity.

   [1]

6. Motor 1 and motor 2 each lift objects of equal weight. They both have the same power rating but motor 2 lifts the weight faster. Which motor is more efficient?

   A   Motor 1

   B   Motor 2

   [1]

7. We continue using non-renewable energy resources despite their negative impact on the environment. Which of the following is a possible reason for this?

   A   Because non-renewable resources will never run out.

   B   Because non-renewable resources are more reliable than renewable alternatives.

   C   Because renewable alternatives are more harmful to the environment.

   [1]

8. A cannon uses explosives to launch a ball into the air. Which is a wasteful energy transfer that occurs when the cannon is fired?

   A   Chemical energy store of explosives → Kinetic energy store of ball

   B   Chemical energy store of explosives → Gravitational potential energy store of ball

   C   Chemical energy store of explosives → Thermal energy store of ball

   [1]

9. Describe the useful energy transfers in a hairdryer.

....

....

....

[2]

10. A 500 g object falls off a cliff and loses 100 J from its gravitational potential energy store. If the gravitational field strength, g = 9.8 N/kg, how high is the cliff?

....

....

....

Height = ... m

[3]

11. A student uses a heater to provide energy to three 0.5 kg blocks made from different materials. She measures their temperatures at regular intervals for five minutes. The graph on the right shows her results. State and explain which block of material has the highest specific heat capacity.

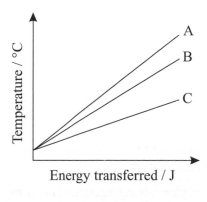

....

....

[2]

15

Test 37: Electricity

There are **11 questions** in this test. Give yourself **10 minutes** to answer them all.

1. True or False? "The UK mains electricity supply is direct current."

    A True

    B False

    [1]

2. True or False? "The current is the same at any point in a single closed loop of wire that is connected to a power supply".

    A True

    B False

    [1]

3. In the UK, what is the typical potential difference between the live wire and earth wire in an electrical appliance?

    A 230 V

    B 0 V

    C 12 V

    [1]

4. A current of 2 A passes through a device with a resistance of 8 Ω. What is the power of the device?

    A 16 W

    B 32 W

    C 128 W

    [1]

5. True or False? "Two components connected in parallel will each have the same potential difference across them."

    A True

    B False

    [1]

6. Increasing the potential difference of electricity at a given power...

    A ... increases the energy lost through heating.

    B ... decreases the current.

    C ... increases the rate of flow of charge.

    [1]

7. The resistance of an ohmic conductor at a constant temperature...

    A ... is higher when larger currents flow through it.

    B ... doesn't change as the current varies.

    C ... is low when the current flows in one direction, but much higher when current flows in the reverse direction.

    [1]

8. In a circuit with a fixed potential difference, what would happen to the current if you increased the resistance?

    A The current would increase.

    B The current would stay the same.

    C The current would decrease.

    [1]

9. A student is investigating the relationship
    between the length of a conductor
    and its resistance.

    The graph on the right shows the
    results of her experiment.

    Describe the relationship between the length
    of the conductor and its resistance.

    Resistance in Ω

    Length of conductor in cm

    ....

    ....

    [1]

10. While in use, a 1.2 V cell transfers 5.4 kJ of energy.
    How much charge passed through the cell in this time?

    ....

    ....

    ....

    Charge = ... C

    [3]

11. The current-potential difference graph
    of a filament lamp is shown on the right.

    Explain why the graph curves as the current increases.

    Current

    Potential difference

    ....

    ....

    ....

    ....

    [3]

    ```
    ___
    15
    ```

Test 38: Electricity

There are **10 questions** in this test. Give yourself **10 minutes** to answer them all.

1. True or False? "Transformers are used to carry electricity all around the country."

    A True

    B False

    [1]

2. What type of resistor could be used in a sensing circuit designed to turn on an automatic night light when it gets too dark?

    A diode

    B thermistor

    C LDR

    [1]

3. What is the name for electric current that is constantly changing direction?

    A Alternating current (ac)

    B Direct current (dc)

    C Switching current (sc)

    [1]

4. True or False? "In a series circuit, the source potential difference is shared between all components."

    A True

    B False

    [1]

5. True or False? "Transmitting electricity at a high potential difference and a low current is more energy efficient than transmitting at a low potential difference and a high current."

    A True

    B False

    [1]

6. Adding resistors in parallel decreases the total resistance of the circuit because...

    A ... it decreases the potential difference through the circuit.

    B ... it increases the total current that can flow around the circuit.

    C ... it decreases the charge that can flow through the circuit.

    [1]

7. Electric current is...

    A ... the driving force that pushes charges around a circuit.

    B ... a measure of how much charges slow down as they flow through a circuit.

    C ... the flow of electrical charge.

    [1]

8. Which wire inside a three-core cable is coated with blue plastic?

    A Earth

    B Live

    C Neutral

    [1]

9. Hair straighteners with a power of 150 W are plugged into a 230 V mains supply.
   Calculate the current through the hair straighteners.

   ....

   ....

   ....

   Current = ... A

   [3]

10. The circuit diagram below shows two resistors connected in series with a battery.

Find the reading on voltmeter V_3.

....

Potential difference = ... V

Find the total resistance, R, of the circuit.

....

Resistance = ... Ω

Find the reading on the ammeter.

....

....

Current = ... A

[4]

15

Physics Paper 1: Electricity

Test 39: Particle Model of Matter

There are **11 questions** in this test. Give yourself **10 minutes** to answer them all.

1. True or False? "Liquids are generally denser than solids and gases."

   A True

   B False

   [1]

2. True or False? "The temperature of a gas is related to the average energy in the kinetic energy stores of its particles."

   A True

   B False

   [1]

3. What is the specific latent heat of fusion?

   A The amount of energy needed to melt 1 kg of a substance.

   B The amount of energy needed to boil 1 kg of a substance.

   C The amount of energy needed to condense 1 kg of a substance.

   [1]

4. The internal energy of a system is equal to...

   A ... the total energy that its particles have in their kinetic energy stores.

   B ... the total energy that its particles have in their potential energy stores.

   C ... the total energy that its particles have in their kinetic and potential energy stores.

   [1]

5. What is the specific heat capacity of a substance?

   A The energy released by a substance when it freezes.

   B The total energy stored by the particles in a system.

   C The energy needed to raise the temperature of 1 kg of a substance by 1°C.

   [1]

6. Changes of state are different to chemical changes because...

   A ... changes of state can be reversed to recover the original properties of the material.

   B ... changes of state result in the creation of new substances.

   C ... changes of state cannot happen to gases.

   [1]

7. What happens to the mass of a substance when it changes from a solid to a liquid?

   A It increases

   B It decreases

   C It stays the same

   [1]

8. What will happen to the pressure of a fixed volume of gas if its temperature is increased?

   A It will decrease

   B It will increase

   C It will stay the same

   [1]

9. A temperature-time graph for a substance that is being cooled down is shown below.
    Identify the state of the substance at point X.

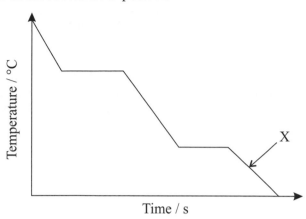

State = ...
[1]

10. A piece of gold has a volume of 2.00×10^{-5} m³ and a mass of 0.386 kg.
    Calculate the density of gold.

    ....

    ....

Density = ... kg/m³
[2]

11. Describe how the density of a solid object of known mass can be measured using a
    eureka can.

    ....

    ....

    ....

    ....

    ....

    ....
[4]

15

Test 40: Atomic Structure

There are **12 questions** in this test. Give yourself **10 minutes** to answer them all.

1. What is the name for atoms with the same number of protons but different numbers of neutrons?

   A   Ions

   B   Isomers

   C   Isotopes

   [1]

2. True or False? "The results of the alpha scattering experiment led to the development of the plum pudding model of the atom."

   A   True

   B   False

   [1]

3. The count rate of a radioactive sample falls from 130 Bq to 65 Bq in 15 minutes. What is its half-life?

   A   15 minutes

   B   30 minutes

   C   1 hour

   [1]

4. True or False? "Any exposure to ionising radiation will kill living cells."

   A   True

   B   False

   [1]

5. True or False? "When a radioactive nucleus emits a beta particle, its atomic number increases."

   A   True

   B   False

   [1]

6. Which type of radiation can penetrate the furthest into materials?

   A   Alpha

   B   Beta

   C   Gamma

   [1]

7. Which type of radiation is the same as a helium nucleus?

   A   Alpha

   B   Beta

   C   Gamma

   [1]

8. Which of the following gives the number of neutrons in the nucleus of an atom?

   A   The mass number

   B   The mass number – the atomic number

   C   The mass number + the atomic number

   [1]

---

9. What is the difference between an atom and an ion?

....

....

[1]

10. The decay of phosphorus-32 is shown below.

$$^{32}_{15}P \rightarrow {}^{.........}_{.........}S + {}^{0}_{-1}e$$

Complete the equation by writing in the missing atomic number and mass number of the product.

[2]

11. Describe how the orbit of an electron around an atom's nucleus changes when the electron absorbs an electromagnetic wave.

....

....

....

[2]

12. Describe the difference between irradiation and contamination.

....

....

....

[2]

15

Test 41: Physics 1 Mixed Topics

There are **11 questions** in this test. Give yourself **10 minutes** to answer them all.

1. What happens to the resistance of a filament lamp as the temperature of the filament increases?

    A   It increases

    B   It decreases

    C   It stays the same

    [1]

2. What happens to a nucleus when it emits a gamma ray?

    A   Its mass decreases

    B   Its charge decreases

    C   Its mass and charge remain unchanged

    [1]

3. A current of 0.21 A flows through a resistor for 3 s. How much charge has passed through the resistor?

    A   0.07 C

    B   0.63 C

    C   1.89 C

    [1]

4. True or False? "The pressure of a gas held at constant volume decreases if the temperature is decreased."

    A   True

    B   False

    [1]

5. What is the power of a device that transfers 20 J in five seconds?

    A   4 W

    B   20 W

    C   100 W

    [1]

6. True or False? "If a resistor is added to a circuit in parallel, the total resistance of the circuit will increase."

    A   True

    B   False

    [1]

7. True or False? "Biofuels are made over millions of years from dead organic material."

    A   True

    B   False

    [1]

8. Which of these is true in the nuclear model of the atom?

    A   The nucleus in the atom is uncharged.

    B   The atom is a ball of positive charge with electrons evenly distributed throughout.

    C   The mass of the atom is concentrated at its centre.

    [1]

9. What happens to the average energy of the particles in a system when the system is heated?

    ....
    [1]

10. The graph on the right shows the number of radioactive nuclei in an archaeological sample over time.
    Use the graph to find the half-life of the radioactive nuclei and calculate the number of radioactive nuclei left in the sample after 16.8×10^3 years.

    ....

    ....

    ....

    ....

    Half-life = ... years

    Number of nuclei = ...
    [3]

11. A spring is extended by 34 mm, causing 0.45 J to be stored in its elastic potential energy store. Assuming the spring's limit of proportionality has not been reached, calculate the spring constant of the spring.

    elastic potential energy = $0.5 \times$ spring constant $\times$ (extension)^2

    ....

    ....

    ....

    ....

    Spring constant = ... N/m
    [3]

    15

Test 42: Physics 1 Mixed Topics

There are **11 questions** in this test. Give yourself **10 minutes** to answer them all.

1. When a person jumps onto a trampoline, energy is transferred from the gravitational potential energy store of the person to the trampoline's elastic potential energy store...

    A   ... electrically.

    B   ... mechanically.

    C   ... by heating.

    [1]

2. True or False? "After a substance is condensed, it can be sublimated to recover its original properties."

    A   True

    B   False

    [1]

3. True or False? "A live wire can still be dangerous even when a switch in the mains circuit is open."

    A   True

    B   False

    [1]

4. Which of the following equations shows the correct relationship between the power of a device (P), its resistance (R) and the current flowing through it (I)?

    A $P = IR$

    B $P = I^2R$

    C $P = IR^2$

    [1]

5. The radius of an atom is approximately...

    A   ... 1×10^{-10} m.

    B   ... 1×10^{-11} m.

    C   ... 1×10^{-12} m.

    [1]

6. True or False? "Some energy is always wasted when an electrical device is used."

    A   True

    B   False

    [1]

7. Which of these is an environmental problem caused by generating electricity using hydro-electric power?

    A   The waste produced is dangerous and difficult to get rid of.

    B   It results in the release of sulfur dioxide, which causes acid rain.

    C   It could result in a loss of habitat for some species.

    [1]

8. Electricity is transferred across step-up transformers to...

    A   ... increase its potential difference for transmission from power stations.

    B   ... increase its potential difference for domestic use.

    C   ... increase its current for transmission from power stations.

    [1]

9. A student has a source of radiation that emits one of the three types of ionising nuclear radiation. She places the source opposite a Geiger-Muller tube and detector and records the count rate. She then places a sheet of paper between the source and the detector and records the count rate, and then repeats this with a sheet of aluminium instead of paper. Describe how her results will allow her to work out which type of radiation is emitted by the source.

....

....

....

....

....

[3]

10. Ethanol has a specific latent heat of vaporisation of 846 000 J/kg.
Calculate the energy required to boil 0.60 kg of ethanol.

thermal energy for a change of state = mass × specific latent heat

....

....

Energy = ... J

[2]

11. An *I-V* graph for a circuit component is shown on the right. Identify the component and give a reason for your answer.

Component: ....

Reason: ....

....

[2]

15

Test 43: Forces

There are **10 questions** in this test. Give yourself **10 minutes** to answer them all.

1. How does the speed of a car affect its stopping distance at maximum braking force?

    A   Higher speed results in a shorter stopping distance.

    B   Higher speed results in a longer stopping distance.

    C   The speed of the car doesn't matter.

    [1]

2. A teapot, weighing 10 N, is sat stationary on a table. What is the normal contact force applied to the teapot by the table?

    A   0 N

    B   −10 N

    C   − 20 N

    [1]

3. Which of these is a typical running speed for a person?

    A   1 m/s

    B   3 m/s

    C   12 m/s

    [1]

4. What is the gradient of a distance-time graph equal to?

    A   Acceleration

    B   Distance

    C   Speed

    [1]

5. Which quantity is not a vector?

    A   Speed

    B   Force

    C   Displacement

    [1]

6. Brakes heat up when they're used because energy is transferred from...

    A   ... the thermal energy stores of the brakes to the kinetic energy stores of the wheels.

    B   ... the kinetic energy stores of the wheels to the thermal energy stores of the brakes.

    C   ... the thermal energy stores of the wheels to the kinetic energy stores of the brakes.

    [1]

7. True or False? "If something's moving there must be an overall resultant force on it."

    A   True

    B   False

    [1]

8. The acceleration of an object is...

    A   ... the change in height over time.

    B   ... the change in position over time.

    C   ... the change in velocity over time.

    [1]

9. Look at this graph.

Describe the acceleration of the object between times A and D.

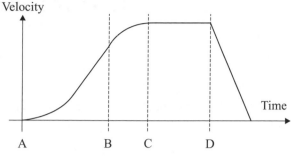

....

....

....

....

....

[3]

10. In an experiment to measure reaction time, Student A suspends a ruler between Student B's thumb and forefinger. Student A drops the ruler without warning, and when Student B catches it the ruler has dropped 28 cm. Calculate Student B's reaction time. The acceleration due to gravity is 9.8 m/s^2.

(final velocity)^2 – (initial velocity)^2 = 2 × acceleration × distance

....

....

....

....

Reaction time = ... s

[4]

15

Physics Paper 2: Forces

Test 44: Forces

There are **11 questions** in this test. Give yourself **10 minutes** to answer them all.

1. In a closed system, the total momentum after a collision is...

    A   ... the same as the total momentum before the collision.

    B   ... always zero.

    C   ... greater than the total momentum before the collision.

    [1]

2. Up to the limit of proportionality, the extension of a stretched spring is...

    A   ... directly proportional to the force applied.

    B   ... inversely proportional to the force applied.

    C   ... unrelated to the force applied.

    [1]

3. What is the correct equation to calculate the weight, W, of an object of mass m in a gravitational field of strength g?

    A $W = g \div m$

    B $W = m \times g$

    C $W = m \div g$

    [1]

4. What is the name of the point at which the weight of an object can be considered to act?

    A   The centre of mass

    B   The centre of weight

    C   The centre of contact

    [1]

5. Which of these does not affect the braking distance of a car?

    A   The car's speed

    B   The condition of the car's tyres

    C   The driver's reaction time

    [1]

6. Stopping distance is equal to...

    A   ... thinking distance + braking distance.

    B   ... thinking distance – braking distance.

    C   ... thinking distance × braking distance.

    [1]

7. A force is applied to an object and causes an acceleration of $2.4 \ \text{m/s}^2$. The same force is applied to a second object with half the mass of the first. What will the acceleration of the second object be?

    A $1.2 \ \text{m/s}^2$

    B $2.4 \ \text{m/s}^2$

    C $4.8 \ \text{m/s}^2$

    [1]

8. When two objects interact, the forces they exert on each other are...

    A   ... equal and in the same direction.

    B   ... equal and in opposite directions.

    [1]

9. A car with a weight of 14 000 N is travelling at a constant speed along a straight road. The car's engine provides a forward force of 2000 N. Complete the free body diagram below to show the force provided by the engine, the total frictional forces acting on the car and the normal contact force. The weight of the car has been drawn for you.

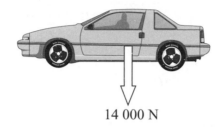

14 000 N

[3]

10. A spring is extended elastically by 0.20 m. It has not been stretched beyond its limit of proportionality. When the spring is extended, 0.60 J is transferred to the spring's elastic potential energy store. Calculate the spring constant of the spring.

elastic potential energy = 0.5 × spring constant × (extension)^2

....

....

Spring constant = ... N/m

[2]

11. This velocity-time graph shows the motion of a car after it starts from rest.

Calculate the distance travelled by the car in the first 30 seconds of its journey.

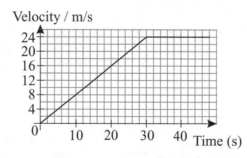

....

....

Distance = ... m

[2]

15

Test 45: Forces

There are **11 questions** in this test. Give yourself **10 minutes** to answer them all.

1. A car accelerates from 9 m/s to 17 m/s in 4 s. What is the average acceleration of the car?

    A 2 m/s^2

    B 8 m/s^2

    C 32 m/s^2

    [1]

2. What is the typical speed of sound in air?

    A 330 m/s

    B 3×10^8 m/s

    C 3.3 m/s

    [1]

3. Which of the following correctly describes inertia?

    A The tendency for objects in motion to speed up.

    B The tendency for objects in motion to slow down.

    C The tendency for objects in motion to continue travelling at the same speed.

    [1]

4. Which of these is false?

    A When an object falls, work is done against gravity.

    B When an object falls, energy is lost from its gravitational potential energy store.

    C When an object is lifted, work is done against gravity.

    [1]

5. If the resultant force on a moving object is zero, the object will...

    A ... slow down and eventually stop.

    B ... keep moving at a steady speed.

    [1]

6. A car is travelling at 30 mph. Which of the following is a sensible estimate for the stopping distance of the car?

    A 5 m

    B 15 m

    C 25 m

    [1]

7. What is a contact force?

    A Any force where two objects interact.

    B A force which can only act when two objects are physically touching.

    C A force which can act when two objects are physically separated.

    [1]

8. What unit is the joule equivalent to?

    A N/kg

    B N/m

    C Nm

    [1]

Physics Paper 2: Forces

Distance / m

9. The graph on the right shows the motion of a cyclist.

Use the graph to find the speed of the cyclist at 8 s.

....

....

....

Speed = ... m/s

[2]

10. Explain why the velocity of an object undergoing circular motion changes but its speed does not.

....

....

....

....

[2]

11. A builder does 84 J of work lifting some bricks from the ground to a height of 1.2 m. Calculate the force exerted by the builder to lift the bricks.

....

....

....

Force = ... N

[3]

15

Physics Paper 2: Forces

Test 46: Waves

There are **11 questions** in this test. Give yourself **10 minutes** to answer them all.

1. True or False? "Waves transfer matter."

    A True

    B False

    [1]

2. The different types of electromagnetic waves...

    A ... all have the same wavelength.

    B ... all have the same frequency.

    C ... form a continuous spectrum.

    [1]

3. What units are used for wave speed?

    A Metres, m.

    B Metres per second, m/s.

    C Hertz, Hz.

    [1]

4. X-rays are suitable to be used in medical imaging because...

    A ... they are ionising.

    B ... some X-rays are always reflected at a boundary between different materials.

    C ... they are not transmitted by bones, but are transmitted by softer tissue.

    [1]

5. In a longitudinal wave, the vibrations are...

    A ... parallel to the direction of energy transfer.

    B ... perpendicular to the direction of energy transfer.

    [1]

6. What is the 'normal' on a ray diagram?

    A The length of a full cycle of a wave.

    B A line drawn perpendicular to a surface at the point of incidence.

    C The dull side of a mirror.

    [1]

7. Waves can change direction as they cross a boundary between two different substances. What is this called?

    A Absorption

    B Reflection

    C Refraction

    [1]

8. Which of the following correctly describes 'radiation dose'?

    A It is the total radiation that a person is exposed to.

    B It is the probability of being exposed to radiation during an average day.

    C It is a measure of the risk of harm to a person from exposure to radiation.

    [1]

Physics Paper 2: Waves

9. Give one use of infrared radiation, and explain how it is suitable for this application.

....

....

....

[2]

10. Describe what happens to the electrons in a radio receiver when it absorbs a radio wave.

....

....

[1]

11. The diagram below shows the equipment used to form a wave on a string.

Describe how you could accurately calculate the speed of the wave on the string.

....

....

....

....

....

....

[4]

15

Physics Paper 2: Waves

Test 47: Waves

There are **11 questions** in this test. Give yourself **10 minutes** to answer them all.

1. Which of these is a use of gamma radiation?

    A Cooking food

    B Communications

    C Medical imaging

    [1]

2. Refraction is the process in which light...

    A ... bounces back as it hits a new medium.

    B ... changes direction as it enters a new medium.

    C ... transfers its energy to the medium as it enters that new medium.

    [1]

3. True or False? "Radio waves are used for television broadcasts."

    A True

    B False

    [1]

4. An electromagnetic wave slows down as it enters a different medium at an angle to the normal. What happens to the wave's direction?

    A It bends away from the normal.

    B It bends towards the normal.

    C It continues travelling at the same angle to the normal.

    [1]

5. Which of these is an example of a longitudinal wave?

    A Ripples on the surface of water

    B Sound waves

    C X-rays

    [1]

6. Prolonged exposure to X-rays can kill body cells because they are...

    A ... ionising.

    B ... longitudinal waves.

    C ... electromagnetic waves.

    [1]

7. Which of the following electromagnetic waves has the lowest frequency?

    A Infrared

    B Visible light

    C Ultraviolet

    [1]

8. Which of the following statements about electromagnetic (EM) waves is correct?

    A All EM waves travel through a vacuum at the same speed.

    B The higher the frequency of an EM wave, the faster it travels through a vacuum.

    C The higher the frequency of an EM wave, the slower it travels through a vacuum.

    [1]

9. Calculate the speed of a wave with a frequency of 3.0×10^7 Hz and a wavelength of 1.4 m.

....

....

....

Wave speed = ... m/s

[3]

10. Calculate the frequency of the wave shown in the graph on the right.

$$\text{period} = \frac{1}{\text{frequency}}$$

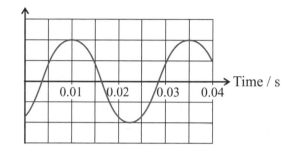

....

....

....

Frequency = ... Hz

[3]

11. A light ray enters the block below at an angle to the normal. The block has a higher optical density than air. Sketch a light ray on the ray diagram below to show how the light ray may refract when it enters the block.

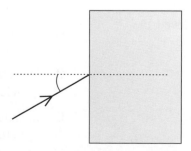

[1]

15

Physics Paper 2: Waves

Test 48: Magnetism and Electromagnetism

There are **11 questions** in this test. Give yourself **10 minutes** to answer them all.

1. The force between the north poles of two bar magnets is...

    A   ... attractive.

    B   ... repulsive.

    [1]

2. Which of the following is a magnetic material?

    A   Nickel

    B   Silver

    C   Copper

    [1]

3. The magnetic field produced when current flows through a wire...

    A   ... is parallel to the wire.

    B   ... is only at each end of the wire.

    C   ... goes round the wire in circles centred on the wire.

    [1]

4. Which of these won't increase the rotational force acting on the rotating coil of wire in an electric motor?

    A   Increasing the current.

    B   Increasing the magnetic field strength.

    C   Reversing the polarity of the magnets.

    [1]

5. True or False? "The magnetic field produced by a solenoid disappears when the current flowing through the solenoid is switched off."

    A   True

    B   False

    [1]

6. A plotting compass can be used to get information about...

    A   ... the strength of a magnetic field only.

    B   ... the direction of a magnetic field only.

    C   ... the strength and direction of a magnetic field.

    [1]

7. A lump of unmagnetised iron becomes an induced magnet when placed next to a bar magnet. When the bar magnet is removed, the magnetic field strength of the iron...

    A   ... decreases.

    B   ... increases.

    C   ... stays the same.

    [1]

8. An iron core can be placed in the middle of a current-carrying solenoid to...

    A   ... change the shape of the magnetic field of the solenoid.

    B   ... increase the strength of the magnetic field of the solenoid.

    C   ... change the direction of the magnetic field of the solenoid.

    [1]

Physics Paper 2: Magnetism and Electromagnetism

9. A current-carrying wire is placed between the north and south poles of two bar magnets at 90° to the magnetic field between the poles. The magnets exert a force of 176 μN on the wire. The length of wire within the magnetic field of the bar magnets is 1.1 cm. The current flowing through the wire is 0.80 A.
    What is the magnetic field strength of the magnetic field caused by the two bar magnets?

    force = magnetic field strength × current × length

    ....

    ....

    ....

    ....

    Magnetic field strength = ... T

    [3]

10. The diagram shows the force on a current-carrying wire in a magnetic field.

    Does the '?' in the diagram mark the north (N) or south (S) pole of the magnet? ....

    Justify your answer.

    ....

    ....

    [2]

11. State the approximate direction in which a compass will point if it is not near to any magnetised materials, and explain why the compass points in this direction.

    ....

    ....

    [2]

    15

Test 49: Physics 2 Mixed Topics

There are **10 questions** in this test. Give yourself **10 minutes** to answer them all.

1. The direction of the arrows on a magnetic field line at a point is given by the direction of the force that would act on...

   A ... a north pole placed at that point.

   B ... a south pole placed at that point.

   C ... a magnetic material placed at that point.

   [1]

2. The magnetic field inside a solenoid is...

   A ... weak and uniform.

   B ... strong and uniform.

   C ... strong and irregular.

   [1]

3. Which of these is a typical walking speed?

   A 1.5 m/s

   B 4.5 m/s

   C 12 m/s

   [1]

4. How much force is needed to elastically stretch a spring with a spring constant of 30 N/m by 0.03 m?

   A 0.001 N

   B 0.027 N

   C 0.9 N

   [1]

5. X-rays are...

   A ... electromagnetic waves.

   B ... sound waves.

   C ... radio waves.

   [1]

6. To travel at a constant speed, the driving force of a car engine must...

   A ... be less than the frictional forces.

   B ... balance the frictional forces.

   C ... exceed the frictional forces.

   [1]

7. Object A is travelling to the left and collides with the stationary object B. After the collision, object B moves away to the left. Which of the following is true of object A's momentum after the collision?

   A It is the same as it was before the collision.

   B It is lower than it was before the collision.

   C It is higher than it was before the collision.

   [1]

8. The amplitude of a wave is...

   A ... the distance between the same point on two adjacent waves.

   B ... the number of waves passing a point per second.

   C ... the maximum displacement of a point on a wave from its undisturbed position.

   [1]

9. A student sets up water waves with a frequency of 4.0 Hz in a ripple tank. She measures the distance shown in the diagram to be 42 cm.

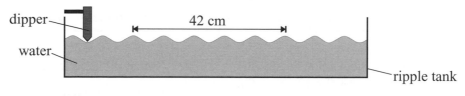

dipper
water
42 cm
ripple tank

Calculate the speed of the waves.

....

....

....

Wave speed = ... m/s

[3]

10. A boat has a driving force of 800 N east. The wind produces a force on the boat of 350 N north. Draw a scale diagram to find the magnitude and direction of the resultant force on the boat. Give your direction as an angle, clockwise from north.

N
W ← → E
S

Magnitude = ... N

Direction = ... ° clockwise from north

[4]

15

Physics Paper 2: Mixed Topics

Test 50: Physics 2 Mixed Topics

There are **11 questions** in this test. Give yourself **10 minutes** to answer them all.

1. True or False? "If an object's slowing down, there must be a non-zero resultant force acting on it."

   A True

   B False

   [1]

2. Which of the following is a contact force?

   A Gravitational force

   B Electrostatic force

   C Air resistance

   [1]

3. Which of the following equations correctly shows the relationship between the momentum, p, mass, m, and velocity, v, of a body?

   A $p = mv$

   B $p = m \div v$

   C $p = v \div m$

   [1]

4. What is the frequency of a wave?

   A The distance travelled by the wave each second.

   B The number of waves passing a point per second.

   C The distance from one crest on a wave to the next adjacent crest.

   [1]

5. Which of these is a typical value for a person's reaction time?

   A 0.04 s

   B 0.4 s

   C 4 s

   [1]

6. Roughly how far would a sound wave travel through the air in 3 s?

   A 110 m

   B 330 m

   C 990 m

   [1]

7. In Fleming's left-hand rule, the directions of which variables are represented by your thumb and first two fingers?

   A Force, magnetic field and displacement

   B Current and magnetic field only

   C Force, current and magnetic field

   [1]

8. Two toy cars with the same mass are pushed with different forces. The car pushed with a greater force has...

   A ... a greater acceleration than the other car.

   B ... a lower acceleration than the other car.

   C ... the same acceleration as the other car.

   [1]

9. A student suspends a spring from a clamp and hangs different weights from it. She plots the force exerted by each weight against the extension of the spring that it produces on the graph on the right. What is the gradient of this graph equal to?

....

[1]

10. A bar magnet is shown below. Draw the magnetic field pattern of the bar magnet on the diagram, including arrows to show the direction of the field.

| N   S |

[2]

11. The diagram on the right shows a Leslie cube. A Leslie cube is a hollow metal cube that can be filled with water. It has four vertical faces. Each face is made from the same material, but they have different colours and surfaces. Describe a method that can be used to compare the amount of radiation emitted from its matt black face to the amount emitted from its shiny white face.

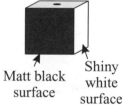

Matt black surface

Shiny white surface

....

....

....

....

....

....

....

[4]

15

Answers

Biology Paper 1

Test 1: Cell Biology
Pages 2–3

1. B *[1 mark]*   2. A *[1 mark]*
3. B *[1 mark]*   4. A *[1 mark]*
5. A *[1 mark]*   6. A *[1 mark]*
7. B *[1 mark]*   8. A *[1 mark]*
9. E.g. a nerve cell is long to cover more distance. / A nerve cell has branched connections at its ends to connect to other nerve cells. *[1 mark]*
10. A stem cell is an undifferentiated cell that can divide to produce more undifferentiated cells *[1 mark]* that can differentiate into other types of cell *[1 mark]*.
11.

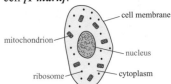

[1 mark for each correct label]
Mitochondria are where most of the reactions for aerobic respiration take place *[1 mark]*. The nucleus contains the genetic material that controls the activities of the cell *[1 mark]*.

Test 2: Organisation
Pages 4–5

1. B *[1 mark]*   2. A *[1 mark]*
3. A *[1 mark]*   4. A *[1 mark]*
5. B *[1 mark]*   6. C *[1 mark]*
7. C *[1 mark]*   8. B *[1 mark]*
9. Protease enzymes catalyse the breakdown of proteins into amino acids *[1 mark]*.
10. Phloem tissue transports (dissolved) sugars from the leaves to the rest of the plant *[1 mark]*.
11. Any two from: e.g. red blood cells / white blood cells / platelets *[2 marks]*

12. Some of the bonds holding the enzyme together break *[1 mark]*. This changes the shape of the enzyme's active site *[1 mark]*. As the enzyme's active site is essential to its function, it won't work anymore *[1 mark]*.

Test 3: Organisation
Pages 6–7

1. B *[1 mark]*   2. C *[1 mark]*
3. B *[1 mark]*   4. C *[1 mark]*
5. C *[1 mark]*   6. B *[1 mark]*
7. B *[1 mark]*   8. A *[1 mark]*
9. E.g. artificial hearts are made from materials such as metal and plastic so they're less likely to be rejected by the body's immune system *[1 mark]*.
10. E.g. drinking too much alcohol *[1 mark]*.
11. A benign tumour is a mass of abnormal cells that doesn't invade other tissues in the body *[1 mark]*.
12. Increasing air movement would increase the rate of transpiration *[1 mark]* because water vapour surrounding the leaf would be swept away *[1 mark]*. This would increase the concentration gradient between water inside and outside the leaf *[1 mark]*, meaning that more water would diffuse out of the leaf *[1 mark]*.

Test 4: Infection and Response
Pages 8–9

1. A *[1 mark]*   2. A *[1 mark]*
3. C *[1 mark]*   4. A *[1 mark]*
5. A *[1 mark]*   6. C *[1 mark]*
7. B *[1 mark]*   8. B *[1 mark]*
9. Tobacco mosaic virus causes a mosaic pattern/discolouration on a plant's leaves *[1 mark]*. This affects growth as it means the plant can't photosynthesise as it otherwise could *[1 mark]*.

10. Mosquitoes are vectors of the protist/pathogen that causes malaria *[1 mark]*. Mosquito nets help to stop people from being bitten by mosquitoes, which stops them from being infected with the protist/pathogen *[1 mark]*.
11. The dead or inactive pathogens that the vaccine contains carry antigens *[1 mark]*. White blood cells produce antibodies in response to these antigens *[1 mark]*. If the same type of pathogens appear after that, the white blood cells can quickly mass-produce the same antibodies to kill the pathogens *[1 mark]*.

Test 5: Infection and Response
Pages 10–11

1. A *[1 mark]*   2. B *[1 mark]*
3. A *[1 mark]*   4. C *[1 mark]*
5. C *[1 mark]*   6. B *[1 mark]*
7. A *[1 mark]*   8. B *[1 mark]*
9. Viruses live inside your cells and replicate themselves *[1 mark]*. The cell then bursts, releasing all the viruses, and this cell damage is what makes you feel ill *[1 mark]*.
10. The nose contains hairs / mucus *[1 mark]*, which trap particles that could contain pathogens *[1 mark]*.
11. A double-blind trial is where neither the doctor nor the patient *[1 mark]* knows whether the patient is getting the drug or the placebo until the results are gathered *[1 mark]*. This is so that the doctors monitoring the patients aren't influenced by their knowledge *[1 mark]*.

Test 6: Bioenergetics
Pages 12–13

1. C *[1 mark]*   2. C *[1 mark]*
3. A *[1 mark]*   4. A *[1 mark]*
5. A *[1 mark]*   6. A *[1 mark]*
7. C *[1 mark]*   8. A *[1 mark]*
9. Because the body can't supply enough oxygen to the muscles *[1 mark]*.
10. Cellulose *[1 mark]*. The cell wall is made using this material *[1 mark]*.

Answers

11. carbon dioxide + water $\xrightarrow{\text{light}}$ glucose + oxygen

    [2 marks for whole equation completed correctly, 1 mark for one or two gaps filled correctly.]

12. Blood flowing through the muscles transports the lactic acid to the liver *[1 mark]*. In the liver, lactic acid is converted to glucose *[1 mark]*.

Test 7: Bioenergetics
Pages 14–15
1. B *[1 mark]* 2. B *[1 mark]*
3. C *[1 mark]* 4. C *[1 mark]*
5. B *[1 mark]* 6. C *[1 mark]*
7. B *[1 mark]* 8. A *[1 mark]*
9. Metabolism is the sum of all of the reactions that happen in a cell or the body *[1 mark]*.
10. It will slow down *[1 mark]* because there will be less light present to transfer the energy needed for photosynthesis *[1 mark]*.
11. Muscle fatigue is where the muscles tire and can no longer contract efficiently *[1 mark]*. It can occur after large periods of exercise *[1 mark]*.
12. Any two from: e.g. in chemical reactions to build up larger molecules from smaller ones. / To allow the muscles to contract/ for movement. / To keep body temperature steady in colder surroundings/to keep warm. *[2 marks]*

Test 8: Biology 1 Mixed Topics
Pages 16–17
1. B *[1 mark]* 2. A *[1 mark]*
3. B *[1 mark]* 4. C *[1 mark]*
5. A *[1 mark]* 6. A *[1 mark]*
7. A *[1 mark]* 8. B *[1 mark]*
9. Any two from: It may have a thin membrane. / It may have a large surface area. / It may have lots of blood vessels. / It could be ventilated. *[2 marks]*
10. Glucose is combined with nitrate ions from the soil *[1 mark]* to make amino acids, which are made into proteins *[1 mark]*.

11. Malignant tumours are cancerous *[1 mark]*. They invade neighbouring tissues in the body *[1 mark]*, and break off and spread to other parts of the body forming secondary tumours *[1 mark]*.

Test 9: Biology 1 Mixed Topics
Pages 18–19
1. C *[1 mark]* 2. A *[1 mark]*
3. A *[1 mark]* 4. C *[1 mark]*
5. A *[1 mark]* 6. B *[1 mark]*
7. B *[1 mark]* 8. C *[1 mark]*
9. Function: Xylem vessels transport water and mineral ions from the roots to the leaves *[1 mark]*. Adaptation: The cells form hollow tubes to allow water and mineral ions to pass through. / The tubes are strengthened by lignin. *[1 mark]*
10. E.g. temperature *[1 mark]*. By using a water bath / an electric heater. *[1 mark]*
11. Layers of fatty material build up inside the coronary arteries, narrowing them *[1 mark]*. This reduces the flow of blood through the coronary arteries *[1 mark]*, resulting in a lack of oxygen for the heart muscle *[1 mark]*.

Biology Paper 2
Test 10: Homeostasis and Response
Pages 20–21
1. B *[1 mark]* 2. C *[1 mark]*
3. B *[1 mark]* 4. B *[1 mark]*
5. A *[1 mark]* 6. B *[1 mark]*
7. B *[1 mark]* 8. C *[1 mark]*
9. It stimulates the basal metabolic rate *[1 mark]*. It plays an important role in growth and development *[1 mark]*.
10. Type 1 diabetes is a condition where the pancreas produces little or no insulin *[1 mark]*. This is dangerous because it means that a person's blood sugar level can rise to a level that can kill them *[1 mark]*.
11. E.g. water content of the blood. Core body temperature. Blood sugar level. *[1 mark each]*

Test 11: Homeostasis and Response
Pages 22–23
1. B *[1 mark]* 2. A *[1 mark]*
3. B *[1 mark]* 4. C *[1 mark]*
5. C *[1 mark]* 6. B *[1 mark]*
7. C *[1 mark]* 8. A *[1 mark]*
9. It stimulates the release of an egg from the ovary *[1 mark]*.
10. A motor neurone *[1 mark]*. Examples: Muscle (e.g. biceps) / A gland (e.g. adrenal gland) *[1 mark]*. Muscles contract (e.g. biceps contract to bend arm) / Glands secrete hormones (e.g. adrenal gland secretes adrenaline) *[1 mark]*.
11. Homeostasis is the regulation of conditions inside the body *[1 mark]* to maintain a stable internal environment *[1 mark]* in response to changes in internal and external conditions *[1 mark]*.

Test 12: Inheritance, Variation and Evolution
Pages 24–25
1. B *[1 mark]* 2. B *[1 mark]*
3. C *[1 mark]* 4. A *[1 mark]*
5. C *[1 mark]* 6. A *[1 mark]*
7. A *[1 mark]* 8. A *[1 mark]*
9. Fossils are the remains or impressions of plants and animals that were alive thousands of years ago *[1 mark]*.
10. Any two from: It has been shown that characteristics/traits are passed on to offspring in genes. / There is evidence in the fossil record. / Because we know how antibiotic resistance evolves in bacteria. *[2 marks]*
11. Any two from: It creates a prejudice that those with a genetic disorder are 'undesirable'. / It may lead to a culture where people select characteristics they want their baby to have (designer babies). / Screening is expensive. *[2 marks]*
12. A vector is used to insert the gene into the required cells / new organism *[1 mark]*. Example: a bacterial plasmid / a virus *[1 mark]*.

Answers

Test 13: Inheritance, Variation and Evolution
Pages 26–27
1. B *[1 mark]* 2. A *[1 mark]*
3. B *[1 mark]* 4. C *[1 mark]*
5. A *[1 mark]* 6. A *[1 mark]*
7. B *[1 mark]* 8. C *[1 mark]*
9. The plant will be tall *[1 mark]*, as the tall allele (T) is dominant over the recessive dwarf allele (t) *[1 mark]*.
10. They have a common distant ancestor *[1 mark]*. They have different recent ancestors *[1 mark]*.
11. During sexual reproduction two gametes fuse together, producing a new cell *[1 mark]*. This cell contains a mixture of chromosomes — some from the mother, and some from the father *[1 mark]*. This means it inherits a combination of features from each parent, producing variation *[1 mark]*.

Test 14: Ecology
Pages 28–29
1. A *[1 mark]* 2. B *[1 mark]*
3. B *[1 mark]* 4. B *[1 mark]*
5. C *[1 mark]* 6. A *[1 mark]*
7. C *[1 mark]* 8. C *[1 mark]*
9. An adaptation is a feature/ characteristic that helps an organism to survive in certain environmental conditions *[1 mark]*.
10. To provide land for cattle / rice crops / farming *[1 mark]*. To grow crops for biofuels *[1 mark]*.
11. E.g. from landfill waste *[1 mark]*. From toxic chemicals (e.g. pesticides and herbicides) *[1 mark]*.
12. When bogs are drained, the peat starts to decompose *[1 mark]*, releasing carbon dioxide which contributes to global warming *[1 mark]*.

Test 15: Ecology
Pages 30–31
1. C *[1 mark]* 2. C *[1 mark]*
3. A *[1 mark]* 4. A *[1 mark]*
5. A *[1 mark]* 6. B *[1 mark]*
7. A *[1 mark]* 8. B *[1 mark]*
9. Interdependence is where each species in a community depends on one another for something *[1 mark]*.
10. It releases carbon dioxide into the air *[1 mark]*.
11. Any two from: Breeding programmes. / Programmes to regenerate rare habitats. / Programmes to reintroduce field margins and hedgerows to farm land. / Programmes to reduce deforestation. / Programmes to reduce carbon dioxide emissions. / Programmes to encourage people to recycle waste. *[2 marks]*
12. Any three from: New pathogens arriving. / New predators arriving. / A reduction in the availability of food sources. / An increase in the number or type of competitors. *[3 marks]*

Test 16: Biology 2
Mixed Topics
Pages 32–33
1. B *[1 mark]* 2. A *[1 mark]*
3. C *[1 mark]* 4. B *[1 mark]*
5. A *[1 mark]* 6. B *[1 mark]*
7. A *[1 mark]* 8. C *[1 mark]*
9. To produce insulin *[1 mark]*.
10. Because people aren't immune to the new strain *[1 mark]* and there is no effective treatment *[1 mark]*.
11. LH and FSH are given to a woman to stimulate several eggs to mature *[1 mark]*. The eggs are collected from the woman's ovaries and fertilised in a laboratory *[1 mark]*. The fertilised eggs are grown into embryos *[1 mark]*. Once the embryos are balls of cells, they are transferred into the woman's uterus *[1 mark]*.

Test 17: Biology 2
Mixed Topics
Pages 34–35
1. C *[1 mark]* 2. B *[1 mark]*
3. C *[1 mark]* 4. C *[1 mark]*
5. B *[1 mark]* 6. B *[1 mark]*
7. C *[1 mark]* 8. C *[1 mark]*
9. So that your cells and the enzymes in them have the right conditions to function properly *[1 mark]*.

10. Any two from: e.g. it allows scientists to identify genes in the genome that are linked to different types of disease. / Knowing which genes are linked to inherited diseases could help us to understand them better and find effective treatments. / Scientists can look at genomes to trace the migrations of certain populations around the world. *[2 marks]*
11.

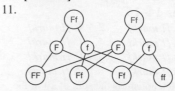

[1 mark for the gametes' alleles being correct and 1 mark for the offspring's genotypes being correct] As the cystic fibrosis allele is recessive, for the child to have the disease they will need two recessive alleles *[1 mark]*. The diagram shows that the chance the child will have cystic fibrosis is 25%, or 1 in 4 *[1 mark]*.

Chemistry Paper 1

Test 18: Atomic Structure and the Periodic Table
Pages 36–37
1. B *[1 mark]* 2. A *[1 mark]*
3. A *[1 mark]* 4. C *[1 mark]*
5. C *[1 mark]* 6. A *[1 mark]*
7. C *[1 mark]* 8. C *[1 mark]*
9. They have the same number of outer electrons / electrons in their outer shell *[1 mark]*.
10. As you move down the group, the outer electron is further away from the nucleus *[1 mark]*. So it is less strongly attracted to the nucleus and is lost more easily *[1 mark]*.
11. Electron — –1 *[1 mark]*
    Proton — +1 *[1 mark]*
    Neutron — no charge / 0 *[1 mark]*
12. $2Li + 2H_2O \rightarrow 2LiOH + H_2$ *[1 mark]*.

Answers

Test 19: Bonding, Structure and Properties
Pages 38–39
1. C *[1 mark]*   2. A *[1 mark]*
3. B *[1 mark]*   4. A *[1 mark]*
5. A *[1 mark]*   6. B *[1 mark]*
7. B *[1 mark]*   8. B *[1 mark]*
9. The two chlorine atoms share a pair of electrons *[1 mark]*. This forms a single covalent bond *[1 mark]*.
10. Sodium chloride is a giant ionic lattice *[1 mark]*, made up of sodium ions and chloride ions *[1 mark]*.
11. The intermolecular forces between polymer molecules are large, so a lot of energy is needed to break them apart *[1 mark]*.
12. Graphite has free/delocalised electrons between layers *[1 mark]* that can move and carry a charge *[1 mark]*.

Test 20: Bonding, Structure and Properties
Pages 40–41
1. A *[1 mark]*   2. B *[1 mark]*
3. C *[1 mark]*   4. A *[1 mark]*
5. C *[1 mark]*   6. B *[1 mark]*
7. B *[1 mark]*   8. A *[1 mark]*
9. The metal atom loses electrons to form a positively charged ion and the non-metal gains these electrons to form negatively charged ion. *[1 mark]*.
10. Fullerenes are molecules of carbon atoms that form hollow shapes *[1 mark]*. The carbon atoms are arranged in hexagonal rings (but can also contain rings with 5 or 7 carbon atoms) *[1 mark]*. They are used e.g. for drug delivery into the body / in lubricants / as catalysts / as nanotubes *[1 mark]*.
11. The layers of atoms in pure metals can slide over one another *[1 mark]*. Alloys are harder because the layers are distorted so can't slide over one another *[1 mark]*.
12. Ethanol (it boils at 78 °C) *[1 mark]*

Test 21: Quantitative Chemistry
Pages 42–43
1. A *[1 mark]*   2. B *[1 mark]*
3. C *[1 mark]*   4. B *[1 mark]*
5. B *[1 mark]*   6. B *[1 mark]*
7. B *[1 mark]*   8. C *[1 mark]*
9. $2 Al_2O_{3(l)} \rightarrow 4 Al_{(l)} + 3 O_{2(g)}$ *[1 mark]*
10. Relative formula mass (M_r)
$= 24 + (2 \times 16) + (2 \times 1) = 58$
[1 mark]
Mass = number of moles × M_r
$= 2.5 \times 58$ *[1 mark]*
$= 145$ g *[1 mark]*
[Or 3 marks for the correct answer via any other method.]
11. Divide the reacting mass of iron by its A_r and divide the reacting mass of oxygen gas by its M_r to give the number of moles:
Fe: $140 \div 56 = 2.5$ moles
O_2: $80 \div 32 = 2.5$ moles *[1 mark]*
So 2.5 moles of Fe reacts with 2.5 moles of O_2. This simplifies to 1:1 *[1 mark]*. So the symbol equation is $2Fe + O_2 \rightarrow 2FeO$ *[1 mark]*.
[Or 3 marks for the correct answer via any other method.]

Test 22: Chemical Changes
Pages 44–45
1. C *[1 mark]*   2. C *[1 mark]*
3. A *[1 mark]*   4. B *[1 mark]*
5. C *[1 mark]*   6. C *[1 mark]*
7. B *[1 mark]*   8. B *[1 mark]*
9. Strong acids ionise completely in water, weak acids do not fully ionise in water *[1 mark]*.
10. Negative electrode: aluminium ions are reduced/gain electrons to form aluminium / $Al^{3+} + 3e^- \rightarrow Al$ *[1 mark]*
Positive electrode: oxygen ions are oxidised/lose electrons to form oxygen / $2O^{2-} \rightarrow O_2 + 4e^-$ *[1 mark]*
11. $H^+_{(aq)} + OH^-_{(aq)} \rightarrow H_2O_{(l)}$ *[1 mark]*

12. Magnesium reacts vigorously with hydrochloric acid, producing bubbles/effervescence *[1 mark]*. The reaction of HCl with iron would be less vigorous/produce fewer bubbles than with magnesium *[1 mark]*. This is because magnesium is more reactive than iron / is higher than iron in the reactivity series *[1 mark]*.

Test 23: Energy Changes
Pages 46–47
1. A *[1 mark]*   2. B *[1 mark]*
3. A *[1 mark]*   4. A *[1 mark]*
5. B *[1 mark]*   6. B *[1 mark]*
7. B *[1 mark]*   8. C *[1 mark]*
9. Find the energy required to break the bonds:
$4(C - H) + 2(O = O)$
$= (4 \times 413) + (2 \times 496)$
$= 2644$ kJ/mol *[1 mark]*
Find the energy released when forming new bonds:
$2(C = O) + 4(O - H)$
$= (2 \times 803) + (4 \times 464)$
$= 3462$ kJ/mol *[1 mark]*
So the energy change =
$2644 - 3462 = -818$ kJ/mol *[1 mark]*
[Or 3 marks for the correct answer via any other method.]
10. E.g. combustion / neutralisation / many oxidation reactions *[1 mark]*.
11.
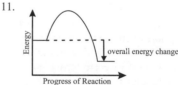
[1 mark for correct axes, 1 mark for correct labelling overall energy change, 1 mark for correct shape of curve linking the reactants to the products.]

Test 24: Chemistry 1 Mixed Topics
Pages 48–49
1. C *[1 mark]*   2. B *[1 mark]*
3. C *[1 mark]*   4. B *[1 mark]*
5. A *[1 mark]*   6. A *[1 mark]*
7. C *[1 mark]*   8. A *[1 mark]*
9. A (metal) salt *[1 mark]* and hydrogen *[1 mark]*.

Answers

10. Group 4 *[1 mark]*, as it has four electrons in its outer shell *[1 mark]*.

11. Relative formula mass (M_r) of CO_2 = 12 + (2 × 16) = 44 *[1 mark]*. Number of moles of C = 66 g ÷ 12 = 5.5. From balanced equation, 5.5 moles of CO_2 are produced *[1 mark]*. Mass of CO_2 = moles × M_r = 5.5 × 44 = 242 g *[1 mark]*.
[Or 3 marks for the correct answer via any other method.]

Test 25: Chemistry 1 Mixed Topics
Pages 50–51

1. B *[1 mark]* 2. A *[1 mark]*
3. C *[1 mark]* 4. B *[1 mark]*
5. A *[1 mark]* 6. C *[1 mark]*
7. A *[1 mark]* 8. A *[1 mark]*

9. It shows an exothermic reaction *[1 mark]*. You can tell this because the products are at a lower energy than the reactants *[1 mark]*.

10. concentration = mass ÷ volume = 0.25 ÷ 0.5 = 0.5 g/dm³.
[2 marks for the correct answer, otherwise 1 mark for correct working.]

11. A metal will displace another metal if it's more reactive *[1 mark]*.

12. Find the number of moles in 1.84 g of ethanol:
moles = mass ÷ M_r
= 1.84 ÷ 46 = 0.04 moles *[1 mark]*
1 mole of ethanol reacts to form 2 moles of carbon dioxide, so 0.04 moles reacts to form 0.04 × 2 = 0.08 moles *[1 mark]*
[Or 2 marks for the correct answer via any other method.]

Chemistry Paper 2

Test 26: Rate and Extent of Chemical Change
Pages 52–53

1. B *[1 mark]* 2. C *[1 mark]*
3. C *[1 mark]* 4. A *[1 mark]*
5. B *[1 mark]* 6. B *[1 mark]*
7. B *[1 mark]* 8. C *[1 mark]*

9. E.g. experiment 2 could have been carried out at a higher temperature / with a greater concentration of reactants / at a higher pressure (with gases) / with a catalyst / with solid reactants crushed into smaller parts *[1 mark]*. This would have increased the rate of reaction, as shown by the steeper graph *[1 mark]*.

10. E.g. carry out the reaction on a mass balance and record the decrease in mass *[1 mark]* and the time it takes for the reaction to finish *[1 mark]*. Calculate the mean rate of reaction by dividing the decrease in mass by the time taken *[1 mark]*. / Using a gas syringe, record the volume of gas given off *[1 mark]* and the time it takes for the reaction to finish *[1 mark]*. Calculate the mean rate of reaction by dividing the volume of gas by the time taken *[1 mark]*.

11. The forwards reaction would be favoured *[1 mark]*. The right hand side contains fewer molecules of gas so the system would form more products in order to reduce the pressure (and so oppose the change) *[1 mark]*.

Test 27: Rate and Extent of Chemical Change
Pages 54–55

1. A *[1 mark]* 2. B *[1 mark]*
3. C *[1 mark]* 4. B *[1 mark]*
5. A *[1 mark]* 6. A *[1 mark]*
7. B *[1 mark]* 8. A *[1 mark]*

9. The forward and reverse reactions are occurring at exactly the same rate *[1 mark]*.

10. The volume of O_2 produced will stay the same *[1 mark]*. The presence of a catalyst doesn't affect the amount of O_2 produced. / The total volume of O_2 produced is only affected by the initial amount of H_2O_2 *[1 mark]*.

11. Increasing the concentration of a solution increases the number of reactant particles in a given volume *[1 mark]* so will increase the frequency of collisions *[1 mark]*.

12. Rate of reaction = amount of product formed ÷ time = 10.2 ÷ 20 *[1 mark]* = 0.51 cm³/s *[1 mark]*.

Test 28: Organic Chemistry
Pages 56–57

1. B *[1 mark]* 2. B *[1 mark]*
3. C *[1 mark]* 4. B *[1 mark]*
5. C *[1 mark]* 6. A *[1 mark]*
7. A *[1 mark]* 8. C *[1 mark]*

9. $C_3H_8 + 5O_2 \rightarrow 3CO_2 + 4H_2O$
[2 marks — 1 mark for formulas, 1 mark for correct balancing]

10. Decane will have a higher boiling point *[1 mark]* because it has a longer hydrocarbon chain *[1 mark]*.

11. There is a temperature gradient in the column/the column gets cooler as you go up it *[1 mark]*. The fractions have different boiling points *[1 mark]* so they condense and drain out at different levels *[1 mark]*.

Test 29: Chemical Analysis
Pages 58–59

1. C *[1 mark]* 2. A *[1 mark]*
3. B *[1 mark]* 4. A *[1 mark]*
5. A *[1 mark]* 6. B *[1 mark]*
7. A *[1 mark]* 8. B *[1 mark]*

9. The water is impure *[1 mark]*.

10. Put damp litmus paper into the gas. Chlorine will turn the litmus paper white / bleach it *[1 mark]*.

11. R_f = 3.2 ÷ 5.0 *[1 mark]* = 0.64 *[1 mark]*

12. Mobile phase and stationary phase *[1 mark]*
A pure substance will leave a single spot on the chromatography paper in all solvents *[1 mark]*. An impure substance can leave multiple spots (depending on the solvent) *[1 mark]*.

Test 30: Chemistry of the Atmosphere
Pages 60–61

1. C *[1 mark]* 2. A *[1 mark]*
3. A *[1 mark]* 4. B *[1 mark]*
5. B *[1 mark]* 6. A *[1 mark]*
7. C *[1 mark]* 8. B *[1 mark]*

Answers

9. E.g. tax companies/individuals based on CO_2 emissions / invest in renewable energy resources/nuclear power / cap emissions made by companies *[1 mark]*. E.g. concern about impact on economic growth / alternative technologies still need development *[1 mark]*.
10. Green plants and algae decreased the carbon dioxide level and increased the oxygen level *[1 mark]* through photosynthesis *[1 mark]*.
11. Carbon dioxide *[1 mark]*. E.g. methane / ammonia / water vapour / nitrogen *[1 mark]*. From volcanic eruptions *[1 mark]*.

Test 31: Chemistry of the Atmosphere
Pages 62–63
1. A *[1 mark]*   2. C *[1 mark]*
3. A *[1 mark]*   4. B *[1 mark]*
5. A *[1 mark]*   6. A *[1 mark]*
7. B *[1 mark]*   8. C *[1 mark]*
9. Rising global temperatures could cause the ice caps to melt *[1 mark]*. This would cause a rise in sea level *[1 mark]*, leading to increased flooding/coastal erosion *[1 mark]*.
10. E.g. increased agriculture *[1 mark]*, as farm animals produce methane through their digestive processes *[1 mark]*. Creating waste *[1 mark]*, as methane is released by decomposition of waste *[1 mark]*.

Test 32: Using Resources
Pages 64–65
1. A *[1 mark]*   2. C *[1 mark]*
3. C *[1 mark]*   4. A *[1 mark]*
5. B *[1 mark]*   6. B *[1 mark]*
7. B *[1 mark]*   8. C *[1 mark]*
9. Any two from: e.g. mining ores damages the landscape. / Extracting the metal from the ore uses energy from burning fossil fuels, resulting in CO_2 emissions. / Disposal of the waste produced destroys habitats. *[2 marks]*
10. E.g. bubbling chlorine gas through it / using ozone / using ultraviolet light *[1 mark]*

11. Extracting and processing the raw materials *[1 mark]*, manufacturing and packaging *[1 mark]*, using the product *[1 mark]*, disposal of the product *[1 mark]*.

Test 33: Chemistry 2 Mixed Topics
Pages 66–67
1. A *[1 mark]*   2. B *[1 mark]*
3. B *[1 mark]*   4. B *[1 mark]*
5. B *[1 mark]*   6. B *[1 mark]*
7. C *[1 mark]*   8. B *[1 mark]*
9. Part 1: effluent *[1 mark]*
   Process used to treat it: aerobic digestion *[1 mark]*
   Part 2: sludge *[1 mark]*
   Process used to treat it: anaerobic digestion *[1 mark]*.
10. Any two from: e.g. green plants/algae absorbed the carbon dioxide during photosynthesis / it dissolved in the ocean / it became locked up in sedimentary rocks/fossil fuels when they formed *[2 marks]*.
11. The components are mixed together in measured quantities *[1 mark]*.

Test 34: Chemistry 2 Mixed Topics
Pages 68–69
1. B *[1 mark]*   2. B *[1 mark]*
3. A *[1 mark]*   4. C *[1 mark]*
5. C *[1 mark]*   6. B *[1 mark]*
7. B *[1 mark]*   8. B *[1 mark]*
9. Line 2 *[1 mark]*. Line 2 has a lower initial rise in energy than line 1, showing a lower activation energy *[1 mark]*.
10. A selective life cycle assessment only shows some environmental impacts of a product *[1 mark]*. Companies may select impacts in a biased way to support their own products or claims *[1 mark]*.
11. It will increase the rate of the reaction *[1 mark]* because the surface area of the solid is increased *[1 mark]*, meaning more frequent collisions between reactants *[1 mark]*.

Physics Paper 1
Test 35: Energy
Pages 70–71
1. B *[1 mark]*   2. C *[1 mark]*
3. A *[1 mark]*   4. A *[1 mark]*
5. C *[1 mark]*   6. A *[1 mark]*
7. C *[1 mark]*   8. B *[1 mark]*
9. $E_k = \frac{1}{2}mv^2$
   $= \frac{1}{2} \times 160 \times 8.5^2$ *[1 mark]*
   $= 5780$ J *[1 mark]*
10. Any two from: e.g. Radioactive waste is produced, which is difficult to dispose of safely. / It's expensive to set up and close down nuclear power stations. / There is a risk of radiation leaks and catastrophes. *[2 marks]*
11. 500 g – 0.5 kg
    Specific heat capacity = energy ÷ (mass × temperature change) *[1 mark]*
    Specific heat capacity
       $= 2925 \div (0.5 \times 15)$ *[1 mark]*
       $= 390$ J/kg°C *[1 mark]*

Test 36: Energy
Pages 72–73
1. C *[1 mark]*   2. A *[1 mark]*
3. A *[1 mark]*   4. B *[1 mark]*
5. A *[1 mark]*   6. B *[1 mark]*
7. B *[1 mark]*   8. C *[1 mark]*
9. A hairdryer transfers energy electrically from the mains to the thermal energy store of the hairdryer heater *[1 mark]* and the kinetic energy store of the fan blades *[1 mark]*.
10. 500 g = 0.5 kg
    change in gravitational potential energy = change in height × mass × g
    Rearrange the formula:
    change in height = change in gravitational potential energy ÷ (mass × g) *[1 mark]*
       $= 100 \div (0.5 \times 9.8)$ *[1 mark]*
       $= 20.40...$
       $= 20$ m (to 2 s.f.) *[1 mark]*
11. Block C *[1 mark]*, as it has the lowest temperature change for the given amount of energy supplied *[1 mark]*.

108

Answers

Test 37: Electricity
Pages 74–75
1. B *[1 mark]* 2. A *[1 mark]*
3. A *[1 mark]* 4. B *[1 mark]*
5. A *[1 mark]* 6. B *[1 mark]*
7. B *[1 mark]* 8. C *[1 mark]*
9. Resistance is directly proportional to the length of the conductor *[1 mark]*.
10. Convert energy into J:
5.4 kJ = 5400 J *[1 mark]*
energy = charge × potential difference / $E = QV$
Rearrange the formula:
$Q = E \div V$
= 5400 ÷ 1.2 *[1 mark]*
= 4500 C *[1 mark]*
11. As more current flows through the lamp, the temperature of the filament increases *[1 mark]*. As the temperature increases, the resistance increases *[1 mark]*. The greater the resistance, the flatter the graph, so the graph curves as the current increases *[1 mark]*.

Test 38: Electricity
Pages 76–77
1. B *[1 mark]* 2. C *[1 mark]*
3. A *[1 mark]* 4. A *[1 mark]*
5. A *[1 mark]* 6. B *[1 mark]*
7. C *[1 mark]* 8. C *[1 mark]*
9. Power = potential difference × current / $P = VI$
Rearrange the formula:
$I = P \div V$ *[1 mark]*
= 150 ÷ 230 *[1 mark]*
= 0.652...
= 0.65 A (to 2 s.f.) *[1 mark]*
10. In a series circuit, the supply potential difference is shared, so:
$V_3 = V_1 + V_2 = 3 + 2 = 5$ V *[1 mark]*
Resistances add up, so:
$R = R_1 + R_2 = 6 + 4 = 10\ \Omega$ *[1 mark]*
The ammeter will measure the total current. The current can be calculated using the supply potential difference and the total resistance of the circuit. (Alternatively, it could be calculated using the potential difference across R_1 or R_2.)
potential difference = current × resistance / $V = IR$

Rearrange the formula:
$I = V \div R$
$= V_3 \div R$
= 5 ÷ 10 *[1 mark]*
= 0.5 A *[1 mark]*

Test 39: Particle Model of Matter
Pages 78–79
1. B *[1 mark]* 2. A *[1 mark]*
3. A *[1 mark]* 4. C *[1 mark]*
5. C *[1 mark]* 6. A *[1 mark]*
7. C *[1 mark]* 8. B *[1 mark]*
9. solid *[1 mark]*
10. density = mass ÷ volume
= 0.386 ÷ (2.00 × 10⁻⁵) *[1 mark]*
= 19 300 kg/m³ *[1 mark]*
11. Fill the eureka can with water to just below the spout, and place a measuring cylinder beneath the spout *[1 mark]*. Submerge the object in the water and collect the displaced water in the measuring cylinder *[1 mark]*. Record the volume of water in the measuring cylinder, which is equal to the volume of the object *[1 mark]*. Substitute the object's mass and volume into density = mass ÷ volume to find its density *[1 mark]*.

Test 40: Atomic Structure
Pages 80–81
1. C *[1 mark]* 2. B *[1 mark]*
3. A *[1 mark]* 4. B *[1 mark]*
5. A *[1 mark]* 6. C *[1 mark]*
7. A *[1 mark]* 8. B *[1 mark]*
9. An atom is electrically neutral, but an ion is charged. / An atom has the same number of protons and electrons, but an ion doesn't *[1 mark]*.
10. $^{32}_{16}$S
[1 mark for each correct number]
11. When an electron in an atom absorbs an electromagnetic wave, the electron moves to a higher energy level *[1 mark]*, and it will orbit further from the nucleus *[1 mark]*.

12. Irradiation is when an object is exposed to radiation emitted by a radioactive source *[1 mark]* while contamination is when (unwanted) atoms of a radioactive source get on/inside another object *[1 mark]*.

Test 41: Physics 1 Mixed Topics
Pages 82–83
1. A *[1 mark]* 2. C *[1 mark]*
3. B *[1 mark]* 4. A *[1 mark]*
5. A *[1 mark]* 6. B *[1 mark]*
7. B *[1 mark]* 8. C *[1 mark]*
9. It increases *[1 mark]*
10. There are initially 14 000 radioactive nuclei, so after one half-life there will be 7000 radioactive nuclei.
Reading from graph:
half-life = 5.6 × 10³ years *[1 mark]*
16.8 × 10³ years is
(16.8 × 10³) ÷ (5.6 × 10³)
= 3 half-lives *[1 mark]*
Number of radioactive nuclei left after 2 half-lives
= 7000 ÷ 2 = 3500
Number of radioactive nuclei left after 3 half-lives
= 3500 ÷ 2 = 1750 *[1 mark]*
11. 34 mm = 0.034 m *[1 mark]*
elastic potential energy = 0.5 × spring constant × (extension)² or $E_e = \frac{1}{2}ke^2$
Rearrange for k:
$k = \frac{2E_e}{e^2} = \frac{2 \times 0.45}{0.034^2}$ *[1 mark]*
= 778.5... N/m
= 780 N/m (to 2 s.f.) *[1 mark]*

Test 42: Physics 1 Mixed Topics
Pages 84–85
1. B *[1 mark]* 2. B *[1 mark]*
3. A *[1 mark]* 4. B *[1 mark]*
5. A *[1 mark]* 6. A *[1 mark]*
7. C *[1 mark]* 8. A *[1 mark]*

Answers

9. E.g. If the count-rate reduces significantly when the paper is used, then the source emits alpha radiation *[1 mark]*. If the count rate is greatly reduced by the aluminium but not the paper, then the source emits beta radiation *[1 mark]*. If the count rate isn't greatly reduced by either sheet then the source emits gamma radiation *[1 mark]*.

10. thermal energy for a change of state
 = mass × specific latent heat
 = 0.60 × 846 000 *[1 mark]*
 = 507 600 J
 = 508 000 J (to 3 s.f.) *[1 mark]*

11. Diode *[1 mark]*. The *I-V* graph shows that current only flows in one direction / there is a very high resistance in the reverse direction *[1 mark]*.

Physics Paper 2

Test 43: Forces
Pages 86–87

1. B *[1 mark]* 2. B *[1 mark]*
3. B *[1 mark]* 4. C *[1 mark]*
5. A *[1 mark]* 6. B *[1 mark]*
7. B *[1 mark]* 8. C *[1 mark]*
9. Between A and B, the acceleration of the object increases at an increasing rate for approximately half the time, then the object has a constant acceleration *[1 mark]*. Between B and C the object's acceleration gradually decreases *[1 mark]*. Between C and D the object travels at a steady speed / has an acceleration of 0 m/s² *[1 mark]*.

10. 28 cm = 28 ÷ 100 = 0.28 m
 (final velocity)² – (initial velocity)² = 2 × acceleration × distance or
 $v^2 - u^2 = 2as$.
 Rearrange for *v* and substitute in the values:
 $v = \sqrt{2as + u^2}$
  $= \sqrt{2 \times 9.8 \times 0.28 + 0^2}$ *[1 mark]*
  $= 2.34...$ m/s *[1 mark]*

$a = \dfrac{\Delta v}{t}$
$a = g = 9.8$ m/s²:
$t = \dfrac{\Delta v}{a} = \dfrac{2.34...}{9.8}$ *[1 mark]*
 $= 0.239...$
 $= 0.24$ s (to 2 s.f.) *[1 mark]*

Test 44: Forces
Pages 88–89

1. A *[1 mark]* 2. A *[1 mark]*
3. B *[1 mark]* 4. A *[1 mark]*
5. C *[1 mark]* 6. A *[1 mark]*
7. C *[1 mark]* 8. B *[1 mark]*
9.

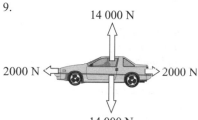

14 000 N

2000 N ◁ ▷ 2000 N

14 000 N

[1 mark for normal contact force arrow drawn the same length as weight and pointing in the opposite direction, 1 mark for a pair of arrows drawn - one pointing left and the other right, 1 mark for drawing these two arrows the same length as each other and shorter than the weight arrow.]

10. elastic potential energy
 = 0.5 × spring constant × (extension)² or $E_e = \frac{1}{2}ke^2$.
 Rearranging for *k* and substituting in the values:
 $k = \dfrac{2E_e}{e^2} = \dfrac{2 \times 0.60}{0.20^2}$ *[1 mark]*
  $= 30$ N/m *[1 mark]*

11. The distance travelled is given by the area under the graph.
 Area of a triangle
 = 0.5 × base × height
 Distance travelled
 = 0.5 × 30 × 24 *[1 mark]*
 = 360 m *[1 mark]*
 [Or 2 marks for the correct answer via any other method.]

Test 45: Forces
Pages 90–91

1. A *[1 mark]* 2. A *[1 mark]*
3. C *[1 mark]* 4. A *[1 mark]*
5. B *[1 mark]* 6. C *[1 mark]*
7. B *[1 mark]* 8. C *[1 mark]*
9. E.g.

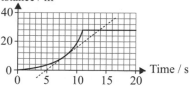

Distance / m

Draw a tangent at 8 s. Tangent passes through (5, 0) and (15, 32), so change in x = 10
change in y = 32
Speed = gradient = 32 ÷ 10 = 3.2 m/s
[1 mark for drawing a tangent at 8 s, 1 mark for correctly calculated speed between 3.0 and 3.4 m/s.]

10. Speed is a scalar, so it has a magnitude but not a direction. Velocity is a vector which has both a magnitude and a direction *[1 mark]*. In circular motion the object's speed remains constant but the direction of the object's motion is constantly changing, so its velocity is changing *[1 mark]*.

11. work done = force × distance
 Rearrange for force and substitute in the values:
 force = work done ÷ distance
  [1 mark]
  = 84 ÷ 1.2 *[1 mark]*
  = 70 N *[1 mark]*

Test 46: Waves
Pages 92–93

1. B *[1 mark]* 2. C *[1 mark]*
3. B *[1 mark]* 4. C *[1 mark]*
5. A *[1 mark]* 6. B *[1 mark]*
7. C *[1 mark]* 8. C *[1 mark]*
9. E.g. to cook food *[1 mark]*. Infrared waves are suitable for this purpose because they transfer energy to an object's thermal energy store when they are absorbed *[1 mark]*.

Answers

10. The electrons oscillate at the same frequency as the frequency of the absorbed wave (producing an alternating current or potential difference) *[1 mark]*.

11. E.g. measure the length of a number of half-wavelengths, and divide this length by the number of half-wavelengths to find the mean half-wavelength *[1 mark]*. Double this value to find the full wavelength *[1 mark]*. Record the frequency being produced by the signal generator *[1 mark]*. Use these values and the equation 'wave speed = frequency × wavelength' to calculate the speed of the wave on the string *[1 mark]*.

Test 47: Waves
Pages 94–95

1. C *[1 mark]*
2. B *[1 mark]*
3. A *[1 mark]*
4. B *[1 mark]*
5. B *[1 mark]*
6. A *[1 mark]*
7. A *[1 mark]*
8. A *[1 mark]*
9. wave speed = frequency × wavelength *[1 mark]*
   $= 3.0 \times 10^7 \times 1.4$
   [1 mark]
   $= 4.2 \times 10^7$ m/s
   (or 42 000 000 m/s)
   [1 mark]

10. The first peak is at 0.01 s and the second peak is at 0.035 s, so:
    period = 0.035 − 0.01
    $= 0.025$ s *[1 mark]*
    frequency = 1 ÷ period
    $= 1 \div 0.025$ *[1 mark]*
    $= 40$ Hz *[1 mark]*
    [Or 3 marks for the correct answer via any other method.]

11. E.g.

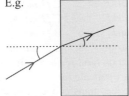

[1 mark for a ray drawn from the point of incidence, inside the block, on the opposite side of and at a smaller angle to the normal than the incident ray].

Test 48: Magnetism and Electromagnetism
Pages 96–97

1. B *[1 mark]*
2. A *[1 mark]*
3. C *[1 mark]*
4. C *[1 mark]*
5. A *[1 mark]*
6. B *[1 mark]*
7. A *[1 mark]*
8. B *[1 mark]*
9. force = 176 μN = 1.76×10^{-4} N
   length = 1.1 cm = 0.011 m *[1 mark]*
   Rearrange the formula:
   $$\text{magnetic field strength} = \frac{\text{force}}{\text{current} \times \text{length}}$$
   $$= \frac{1.76 \times 10^{-4}}{0.80 \times 0.011}$$
   [1 mark]
   magnetic field strength = 0.020 T
   [1 mark]

10. N *[1 mark]*. Fleming's Left Hand Rule shows that the field goes from right to left so ? must be a north pole *[1 mark]*.

11. The compass will point north *[1 mark]*. This is because it aligns with the Earth's magnetic field / the magnetic field generated by the Earth's core *[1 mark]*.

Test 49: Physics 2 Mixed Topics
Pages 98–99

1. A *[1 mark]*
2. B *[1 mark]*
3. A *[1 mark]*
4. C *[1 mark]*
5. A *[1 mark]*
6. B *[1 mark]*
7. B *[1 mark]*
8. C *[1 mark]*
9. The measured distance covers 5 wavelengths, so
   wavelength = 42 ÷ 5
   $= 8.4$ cm *[1 mark]* = 0.084 m
   wave speed = frequency × wavelength
   $= 4.0 \times 0.084$ *[1 mark]*
   $= 0.336$ m/s
   $= 0.34$ m/s (to 2 s.f) *[1 mark]*
   [Or 3 marks for the correct answer via any other method.]

10. E.g. using scale 1 cm = 10 N

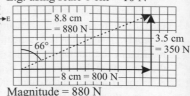

Magnitude = 880 N
Direction = 66° from North
[1 mark for drawing vertical force and horizontal force correctly, 1 mark for drawing resultant force correctly, 1 mark for giving magnitude of force between 870 and 890 N and 1 mark for giving direction between 65° and 67°.]

Test 50: Physics 2 Mixed Topics
Pages 100–101

1. A *[1 mark]*
2. C *[1 mark]*
3. A *[1 mark]*
4. B *[1 mark]*
5. B *[1 mark]*
6. C *[1 mark]*
7. C *[1 mark]*
8. A *[1 mark]*
9. The spring constant of the spring (in N/m) *[1 mark]*

10.

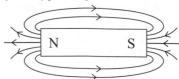

[1 mark for lines (at least 3) drawn to show the correct field shape, 1 mark for arrows drawn in correct direction on every field line.]

11. E.g. Fill the Leslie cube with boiling water *[1 mark]*. Wait for the cube to warm up, then hold a thermometer against both faces to check that they are the same temperature *[1 mark]*. Hold an infrared detector a set distance away from one of the cube's vertical faces, and record the amount of IR radiation it detects *[1 mark]*. Repeat this measurement for the other face at the same distance from the cube *[1 mark]*.